Walch Hands-on Science Series

Force and Motion

Steven Souza, Ph.D.

and

Karen Kwitter, Ph.D.
Williams College
Williamstown, MA

illustrated by Lloyd Birmingham

Project Editors: Joel Beller and Carl Raab

J. WESTON
WALCH
PUBLISHER
Portland, Maine

User's Guide
to
Walch Reproducible Books

As part of our general effort to provide educational materials that are as practical and economical as possible, we have designated this publication a "reproducible book." The designation means that purchase of the book includes purchase of the right to limited reproduction of all pages on which this symbol appears:

Here is the basic Walch policy: We grant to individual purchasers of this book the right to make sufficient copies of reproducible pages for use by all students of a single teacher. This permission is limited to a single teacher and does not apply to entire schools or school systems, so institutions purchasing the book should pass the permission on to a single teacher. Copying of the book or its parts for resale is prohibited.

Any questions regarding this policy or requests to purchase further reproduction rights should be addressed to:

Permissions Editor
J. Weston Walch, Publisher
321 Valley Street • P. O. Box 658
Portland, Maine 04104-0658

1   2   3   4   5   6   7   8   9   10
ISBN 0-8251-3762-4

Acknowledgment

The authors are grateful for the love and support of their parents: Arthur and Sonia Kwitter, and Manuel and Barbara Souza.

The authors thank their sons Randy and Aaron for their encouragement and for trying out some of these activities.

Contents

To the Teacher .... *vii*

1. Vectors 1: Making Vectors 1

2. Vectors 2: Adding Vectors 6

3. Velocity and Acceleration 13

4. Newton's First Law: Inertia 17

5. Newton's Second Law: The Effect of Force 21

6. Pressure Is Not the Same As Force 26

7. Newton's Third Law: Action and Reaction 32

8. Friction 37

9. Center of Mass 43

10. Earth's Gravity and Uniform Acceleration 47

11. Ballistics 52

12. The Pendulum 57

13. Orbital Motion 62

14. Momentum 68

15. Work (the Physics Kind) 72

16. Kinetic Energy 76

17. Potential Energy 80

18. Electric and Magnetic Forces 83

To the Teacher

This is one in a series of hands-on science activity books for middle-school and early-high-school students. A recent national survey of middle-school students conducted by the National Science Foundation (NSF) found that

- more than half listed science as their favorite subject.

- more than half wanted more hands-on activities.

- 90 percent stated the best way for them to learn science was to do experiments themselves.

The books in this series seek to capitalize on that NSF survey. The books are not texts but supplements, written by teachers. They offer hands-on, fun activities that will turn some students on to science. You and your students should select which activities are to be carried out. All of the activities need not be done; pick and choose those that best meet the needs of your students. All of these activities can be done in school, and some can be done at home.

Students will need only basic, standard scientific equipment that can be found in most middle and high school science laboratories. The activities range from the simple (examining Newton's First Law of Inertia) to the difficult (exploring the concept of ballistics). There is something for every student.

THE ACTIVITIES CAN BE USED:

- to provide hands-on experiences pertaining to textbook content.

- to give verbally limited children a chance to succeed and gain extra credit.

- as the basis for class or school science fair projects or for other science competitions.

- to involve students in science club undertakings.

- as homework assignments.

- to involve parents in their child's science education and experiences.

Students can learn important scientific principles from carrying out these activities. Some examples include key concepts in conservation of energy, the laws of motion that govern all moving objects, and the important but sometimes overlooked force of friction.

Each activity has a Teacher Resource section that includes, besides helpful hints and suggestions, a scoring rubric, quiz questions, and Internet addresses for Web sites related to the activity topic. Instructional objectives and the National Science Standards that apply to each activity are provided to help you meet state and local expectations.

INSTRUCTIONAL OBJECTIVES

Students will be able to

- distinguish between a scalar and a vector.
- construct a two-dimensional vector given its X and Y components.
- evaluate the magnitude of a vector given its X and Y components.

 NATIONAL SCIENCE STANDARDS ADDRESSED

Students demonstrate skills that involve

- using the number line and Cartesian coordinates.
- using tools to solve problems.
- carrying out numerical calculations.

Students demonstrate scientific inquiry and problem-solving skills by

- working in teams to collect and share information and ideas.
- using technology and tools to observe and measure objects.

Students demonstrate effective mathematical communication by

- being familiar with common conventions for graphing.

 MATERIALS

For each group:

- Room with a tiled floor or floor with a repeating square or rectangular pattern
- Meterstick
- Masking tape ($\frac{1}{2}$-inch wide preferred)
- Pencil

HELPFUL HINTS AND DISCUSSION

Time frame: 40 minutes, or a single period of instruction
Structure: Groups of two or three students
Location: In class or at home

Make sure that the students have access to an appropriate floor, which may be tiled or have a rectilinear pattern. Each group requires only about 1 square meter of floor space, so many groups can work in one room. Don't worry about the size of the tiles or pattern; their function is to get the taped axes perpendicular to each other and help line up the meterstick parallel to the axes.

ADAPTATIONS FOR HIGH AND LOW ACHIEVERS

High Achievers: High achievers can be encouraged to do the Follow-up Activities, especially number 2.

Low Achievers: Review the relevant concepts for these students, particularly the concept that vectors have two quantities associated with them: magnitude and direction. Have students practice drawing perpendicular components on a Cartesian grid and then drawing in and measuring the vector having those components. For example, use a 3-4-5 right triangle, with 3 and 4 as the perpendicular components; then 5 will be the length of the vector. 5-12-13 is another such combination. Also review the Pythagorean theorem.

SCORING RUBRIC

Full credit can be given to students whose vectors look reasonable and who answer the questions correctly and in complete sentences. The quiz can be scored from 1 to 4 correct.

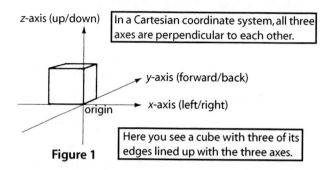

z-axis (up/down)

In a Cartesian coordinate system, all three axes are perpendicular to each other.

y-axis (forward/back)

x-axis (left/right)

origin

Here you see a cube with three of its edges lined up with the three axes.

Figure 1

 **INTERNET TIE-INS**   http://www.glenbrook.k12.il.us/gbssci/phys/Class/vectors/vectoc.html
http://www.frontiernet.net/~imaging/vector_calculator.html
http://comp.uark.edu/~jgeabana/java/VectorCalc.html

 QUIZ   1. A quantity with both magnitude and direction is called a _____.
2. In everyday experience, a position vector has up to _____ components.
3. In a Cartesian coordinate system, all components are zero at the _____.
4. True or false: Two vectors with the same length but different direction are not equal to each other.

Figure 2

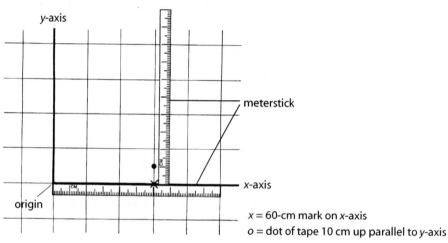

y-axis

meterstick

x-axis

origin

x = 60-cm mark on x-axis
o = dot of tape 10 cm up parallel to y-axis

Figure 3

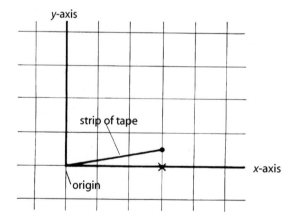

y-axis

strip of tape

x-axis

origin

Name _____   Date _____

Vectors 1: Making Vectors

 BEFORE YOU BEGIN

If a friend asked you how much candy you had and you answered "a kilogram," you might be asked to share it. If your friend asked you for directions to the public library and you said "a kilo-meter," you might get a very puzzled look. Why? Some quantities, like the amount of candy you had, can be fully described using a single number, called a **magnitude**. These are called **scalar** quantities, or **scalars**. Mass, temperature, and age are good examples of scalars. Other quantities, like the instructions for getting to the library, have both a magnitude and a direction. They there-fore require two or more numbers, or **components**, to be fully described. These quantities are called **vectors**. Two vectors are considered identical if they have both the same magnitude and the same direction, even if they have different starting points.

The physical space we exist in has three dimensions, so many of the vectors we encounter consist of three components. We can think of these as up/down, right/left, and forward/back. A convenient coordinate system to describe this physical space has three principal axes (usually called x, y, and z). The **axes** are straight lines that are perpendicular to each other. This kind of coordinate system, named after the seventeenth-century philosopher René Descartes, is called a **Cartesian coordinate system**. The zero points of all three axes in a Cartesian system meet at a point called the **origin**, as shown in Figure 1.

The answer to your friend's question could be: "Go south three blocks, then turn left onto Main Street, and go east until you pass the park. Then go up to the third floor of the municipal building." By specifying changes in position in three independent directions (*south, left/east,* and *up*), you have described a vector in three-dimensional space.

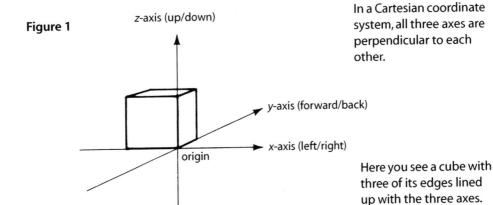

Figure 1

In a Cartesian coordinate system, all three axes are perpendicular to each other.

Here you see a cube with three of its edges lined up with the three axes.

 **MATERIALS**

For each group:
- Room with a tiled floor or floor with a repeating square or rectangular pattern
- Meterstick

- Masking tape (½-inch wide preferred)
- Pencil

(continued)

Name _____ Date _____

 **PROCEDURE**

In this activity, you will work in two dimensions for convenience. The concepts you will explore are also true when extended to three dimensions. You will use the tiled floor as "graph paper" to keep the horizontal and vertical lines perpendicular to each other.

1. Make a two-dimensional coordinate system on the floor as shown in Figure 2. The two axes of the coordinate system must be perpendicular to each other. Look at the lines made by the seams between the tiles or the rectilinear pattern. Pick an intersection between one horizontal line and one vertical line. Designate this as the origin by placing a small dot of tape on that point. Now, place a strip of tape about a meter long on the horizontal line starting at the dot and extending to the right. This will be your *x*-axis. Similarly, tape down a *y*-axis, also starting at the origin and extending away from you perpendicular to the *x*-axis.

2. Make a vector. Place a meterstick on the floor along your *x*-axis, with its point at the origin. Make a small pencil mark on the *x*-axis tape (not on the floor!) at the 60-cm mark. This length represents the *x* component of the vector.

3. Holding the meterstick parallel to the *y*-axis, place it with its zero point on the pencil mark you just made in step 2 and as shown in Figure 2. Put a small dot of tape on the floor at the 10-cm mark. This length represents the *y* component of the vector.

4. Now place a strip of tape on the floor from the origin to the dot you made in step 3. Be careful to tear the tape off at just the right length. You have now made your first vector, as shown in Figure 3. Measure its length and record your result in the Data Collection and Analysis section.

➤ **EXTENSION** Repeat steps 2 through 4, but use an *x* component of 10 cm and a *y* component of 60 cm.

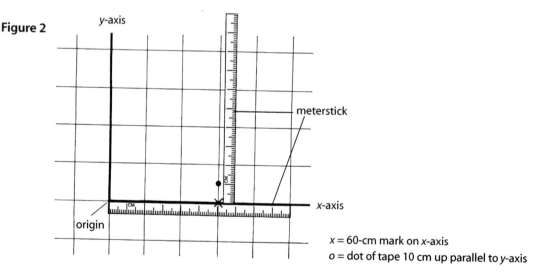

Figure 2

y-axis

meterstick

x-axis

origin

x = 60-cm mark on *x*-axis
o = dot of tape 10 cm up parallel to *y*-axis

(continued)

Name _____ Date _____

Figure 3

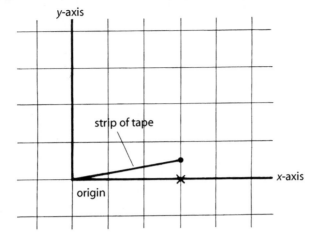

DATA COLLECTION AND ANALYSIS

• Length of vector _____ cm

EXTENSION

• Length of vector _____ cm

CONCLUDING QUESTIONS

1. The vector you created is the hypotenuse of a right triangle whose other two sides are the x and y components given in steps 2 and 3. Compare the length you measured for your vector with the length you would predict from the Pythagorean theorem ($x^2 + y^2 = \text{hypotenuse}^2$). Do the lengths agree? Why might they not be exactly equal? _____

_____

_____

EXTENSION How does the length of the second vector you made compare with the length of the first? Is the second vector identical to the first vector? Why or why not? _____

_____

_____

⚙ Follow-up Activities ⚙

1. List five quantities you encounter in everyday life that are scalars. List five that are vectors.

2. There are other coordinate systems in two dimensions besides the Cartesian system, where components are measured along two perpendicular axes. Research and write a brief report about another two-dimensional coordinate system.

Vectors 2: Adding Vectors

 ## INSTRUCTIONAL OBJECTIVES

Students will be able to

- construct a two-dimensional vector given its x and y components.
- understand how two-dimensional vectors can be added.
- evaluate the magnitude of a vector sum given its x and y components.

 ## NATIONAL SCIENCE STANDARDS ADDRESSED

Students demonstrate skills that involve

- using the number line and Cartesian coordinates.
- using tools to solve problems.
- carrying out numerical calculations.

Students demonstrate scientific inquiry and problem-solving skills by

- working in teams to collect and share information and ideas.
- using technology and tools to observe and measure objects.

Students demonstrate effective mathematical communication by

- being familiar with common conventions for graphing.
- communicating logical arguments clearly.

 ## MATERIALS

For each group:

- Room with a tiled floor or floor with a repeating square or rectangular pattern
- Meterstick
- Masking tape ($\frac{1}{2}$-inch wide preferred)
- Pencil

HELPFUL HINTS AND DISCUSSION

Time frame: 40 minutes, or a single period of instruction
Structure: Groups of two or three students
Location: In class or at home

Make sure that the students have access to an appropriate floor, which may be tiled or have a rectilinear pattern. Each group requires only about 1 square meter of floor space, so many groups can work in one room. Don't worry about the size of the tiles or pattern; their function is to get the taped areas perpendicular to each other and help line up the meterstick parallel to the area.

ADAPTATIONS FOR HIGH AND LOW ACHIEVERS

High Achievers: High achievers can be encouraged to do the Extensions and the Follow-up Activities, especially number 3.

Low Achievers: Review the relevant concepts for these students, particularly that vectors have both magnitude and direction. Have them review drawing perpendicular components on a Cartesian grid and then constructing the vector having those components. For example, use a 3-4-5 right triangle, with 3 and 4 as the perpendicular components; then 5 will be the length of the vector. Another such combination is 5-12-13.

SCORING RUBRIC

Full credit can be given to students whose vectors look reasonable and who answer the questions correctly and in complete sentences. The quiz can be scored from 1 to 4 correct.

Figure 1

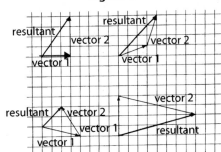

Figure 2

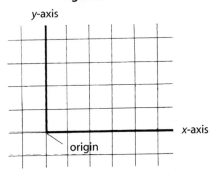

INTERNET TIE-INS   http://www.glenbrook.k12.il.us/gbssci/phys/Class/vectors/vectoc.html
http://www.frontiernet.net/~imaging/vector_calculator.html
http://comp.uark.edu/~jgeabana/java/VectorCalc.html

QUIZ

1. What are the two quantities that describe a vector?
2. Describe the process of adding two vectors, if you know the x and y components of each of them.

True or false:

3. When you add two vectors, the resulting vector sum always has a magnitude equal to the sum of the magnitudes of the original two vectors.
4. All vectors with the same length are identical.

Name _____   Date _____

Vectors 2: Adding Vectors

 BEFORE YOU BEGIN

Suppose you want to go to the movies with a friend. You each have some money and want to know if together you have enough to pay for two tickets. The money you have is a **scalar**, a quantity that can be specified by just a magnitude, or amount. Other kinds of quantities require two pieces of information. On the weather report, you might hear something like "The wind is blowing at 20 miles per hour from the northwest." Describing wind velocity requires not only a magnitude but a direction as well. Wind velocity is a **vector** quantity. The magnitude of the wind velocity is the speed, "20 miles per hour." The direction of the wind velocity is "from the northwest."

To calculate the total amount of money you and your friend have, you just add. Scalar quantities, like an amount of money, can be added directly. You probably realize that it doesn't matter whose money you add first. When you perform addition, you will get the same answer regardless of the order in which you add the numbers.

Vectors can be added together, too, though the rules are a little different from the rules for adding scalars. To add two vectors, you place the starting point of the second vector at the ending point of the first vector. The sum, or **resultant**, is the vector that starts at the beginning of the first vector and ends at the end of the second vector. To find the magnitude of the resultant vector, you can measure it directly. Figure 1 shows four examples of adding vectors graphically. It turns out that just as in scalar addition, the order in which you add makes no difference. You will get the same magnitude and direction for the vector sum whether you add the second vector to the first or the first to the second.

You can also find the magnitude of the resultant vector algebraically, using the x and y components of the individual vectors. The x component of the resultant vector is the sum of the x components of the vectors you are adding. Likewise, the y component of the resultant is the sum of the individual y components. The magnitude of the resultant can be found using the Pythagorean theorem, as described in the Concluding Questions.

Figure 1

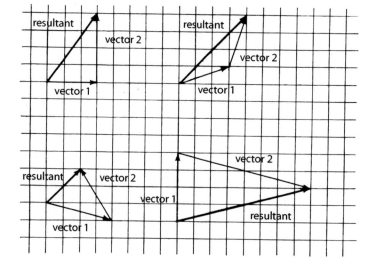

(continued)

                   Walch Hands-on Science Series: Force and Motion

Vectors 2: Making Vectors *(continued)*

 MATERIALS

For each group:
- Room with a tiled floor or floor with a repeating square or rectangular pattern
- Meterstick
- Masking tape ($\frac{1}{2}$-inch wide preferred)
- Pencil

 PROCEDURE

In this activity, you will work in two dimensions for convenience. The concepts you will explore are also true when extended to three dimensions. You will use the tiled floor as "graph paper" to keep the horizontal and vertical lines perpendicular to each other.

1. Make a two-dimensional coordinate system on the floor. The two axes of the coordinate system must be perpendicular to each other. Look at the lines made by the seams between the tiles or the rectilinear pattern. Pick an intersection between one horizontal line and one vertical line. Designate this as the origin by placing a small dot of tape on that point. Now place a strip of tape about a meter long on the horizontal line starting at the dot and extending to the right. This will be your *x*-axis. Similarly, tape down a *y*-axis, also starting at the origin and extending away from your perpendicular to the *x*-axis. See Figure 2.

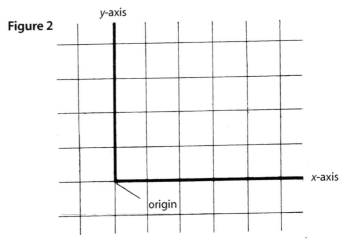

Figure 2

2. Construct the first vector starting at the origin. The *x* component of this vector is 40 cm. The *y* component is 10 cm. Using the meterstick, measure 40 cm from the origin along the *x*-axis and make a small mark on the tape. Then from this mark measure 10 cm up parallel to the *y*-axis. Place a small dot of tape on the floor at this point. Place a strip of tape from the origin to the dot. Draw a little arrowhead on the tape at the endpoint of this first vector.

3. Measure the length of this first vector with the meterstick and record it in the appropriate space in the Data Collection and Analysis section.

4. Construct the second vector, this time using the endpoint of your first vector as the starting point for the second vector. The *x* component of this vector is 20 cm, and its *y* component is 70 cm. To do this, measure 20 cm parallel to the *x*-axis from the endpoint of the first vector, and then 70 cm parallel to the *y*-axis. Again, place a small dot of tape on the floor at this point. Place a strip of tape from the endpoint of the first vector to the dot. Draw a little arrowhead on the tape at the endpoint of this second vector.

(continued)

Vectors 2: Making Vectors (continued)

5. Measure the length of this second vector with the meterstick, and record it in the appropriate space in the Data Collection and Analysis section.

6. Construct the vector sum (the **resultant**) of the two vectors you just made. Place a strip of tape from the origin (the starting point of the first vector) to the endpoint of the second vector. Draw a little arrowhead on the tape at the endpoint.

7. Measure the length of this vector sum with the meterstick and record it in the appropriate space in the Data Collection and Analysis section.

8. Measure the x and y components of the resultant vector and record them in the Data Collection and Analysis section.

EXTENSION

Add the two vectors again, but in the reverse order. Start with the vector called for in step 4, placing its starting point at the origin. Then use its endpoint as the starting point for constructing the vector described in step 2, and construct the vector sum as in step 6. Measure its length and record it below in the Data Collection and Analysis section. Also measure and record the x and y components. Compare the magnitude, the x and y components, and the direction of this vector sum with the vector sum you found in step 7.

DATA COLLECTION AND ANALYSIS

Length of first vector from step 3: _____ cm

Length of second vector from step 5: _____ cm

Length of resultant vector from step 7: _____ cm

X component of resultant vector from step 8: _____ cm

Y component of resultant vector from step 8: _____ cm

EXTENSION

Length of resultant vector: _____ cm

X component of resultant vector: _____ cm

Y component of resultant vector: _____ cm

(continued)

Vectors 2: Adding Vectors *(continued)*

❔ CONCLUDING QUESTIONS

1. The resultant you have created is the hypotenuse of a right triangle whose other two sides are the x and y components of the vector. Compare the length you measured for the resultant with the length you would predict from the Pythagorean theorem ($x^2 + y^2 = \text{hypotenuse}^2$). What reasons might there be for any difference between the measured and calculated lengths?

   _____

   _____

   _____

   _____

2. Was the x component of the resultant vector equal to the sum of the x components of vectors from which it was made? What about the y component? _____

   _____

   _____

   _____

3. Was the length of the resultant vector equal to the sum of the lengths of vectors from which it was made? Why or why not? _____

   _____

   _____

   _____

4. Describe how vector addition differs from the addition of scalar numbers. _____

   _____

   _____

   _____

➪ EXTENSION

Based on your results, what can you conclude about the order in which vectors are added?

_____

_____

_____

(continued)

Vectors 2: Adding Vectors *(continued)*

〰️ Follow-up Activities 〰️

1. Create some vector addition problems like those in this exercise and then do them. Write at least one problem as a word problem, adding real-world vector quantities, like velocities.

2. Create a vector addition problem that adds three vectors. The same rules apply as for adding two vectors.

⟹ EXTENSIONS

• Explore the concept of vector **subtraction**. To subtract one vector from another, you reverse the signs of all of its components, and then add it to the other vector. This is the same idea as subtracting a number B from another number A by reversing B's sign, and then adding it to A. For example, to subtract 2 from 5, you can reverse the sign of the 2—making it –2—and then add it to 5. So you have $5 + (-2) = 3$. You can extend your coordinate system on the floor to include the negative parts of the x- and y-axes.

• Explain why vector addition cannot work like scalar addition. As part of your answer, describe how the magnitude of the vector sum depends on the angle between the two vectors you are adding.

Velocity and Acceleration

 INSTRUCTIONAL OBJECTIVES

Students will be able to

- define and distinguish between velocity and acceleration.
- calculate velocity and acceleration from measurements of position and time.
- draw conclusions based on data.
- record data in a table.

 NATIONAL SCIENCE STANDARDS ADDRESSED

Students demonstrate an understanding of

- motions and forces.
- relevant concepts to explain observed phenomena.
- analysis of data using graphs.

Students demonstrate scientific inquiry and problem-solving skills by

- arguing from evidence and data.
- representing data and results in multiple ways.

 MATERIALS

- Graph paper (finely ruled)
- Plain and colored pencils

HELPFUL HINTS AND DISCUSSION

Time frame: 40 minutes, or a single period of instruction
Structure: Individuals
Location: In class or at home

It might be helpful to review the concepts of velocity as a change in distance per unit time and acceleration as a change in velocity per unit time—and to remind the students of the units for each. Velocity is expressed in meters per second (m/s), while acceleration is expressed in meters per second per second (m/s/s), sometimes written as meters per second *squared* (m/s^2). Students should also review the properties of vectors.

ADAPTATIONS FOR HIGH AND LOW ACHIEVERS

High Achievers: High achievers can be encouraged to do the Extension and the Follow-up Activities.

Low Achievers: Review with these students the concepts of velocity and acceleration and the units in which they are expressed. In addition, you may want to do the first entries in the table on page 15 together with the class.

SCORING RUBRIC

Full credit can be given to students who complete the entries in the data table and who answer the questions correctly and in complete sentences. Extra credit can be given to students who complete the Extension or Follow-up Activities. The quiz can be scored from 1 to 5 correct.

 **INTERNET TIE-INS**   http://www.glenbrook.k12.il.us/gbssci/phys/Class/BBoard.html
http://www.execpc.com/~culp/rockets/physics.html

 QUIZ   1. Why does acceleration have units of distance per unit time per unit time?
2. True or false: (a) Position is the rate of change of acceleration.
   (b) Velocity is the rate of change of position.
   (c) Speed is the magnitude of velocity.
   (d) Acceleration is not a vector quantity.

Velocity and Acceleration

⤳ BEFORE YOU BEGIN ⤳

Imagine that you have just boarded an airplane to visit your relatives. The airplane starts the trip at one position (the airport gate at which you just boarded) and ends at another (the airport gate at your destination). It is often the *change* in position of an object, such as the airplane with you in it, that you wish to know. More specifically, it is the *rate* of change of position that is of interest, because if it is constant you can use this knowledge to predict the position of an object like the airplane at some future time. This rate of change of position, expressed as distance-per-unit time, is called **velocity**. To predict the change in position of the airplane, we also need to know the direction in which it is going, so velocity is expressed as a **vector** quantity. Just as we can treat the components of position (which is also a three-dimensional vector quantity) independently, we can do the same with the three components of velocity. In many cases, we care only about the **magnitude** of an object's velocity, which is called **speed**. The speed of the airplane you are traveling in is probably several hundred miles per hour.

The velocity of the airplane during the trip is not constant. The airplane changes its speed as it moves down the runway. It changes direction as it turns and gains altitude. Just as you can consider the rate of change of *position* of an object, you can also consider the rate of change of its *velocity*. The rate of change of velocity is called **acceleration**, which is especially important because many processes in nature directly result in acceleration. Since velocity is a vector, acceleration will also be a vector. Acceleration results from a change in speed, a change in direction, or a change in both.

✂ MATERIALS

- Graph paper (finely ruled)
- Plain and colored pencils

◈ PROCEDURE

1. We will examine the motion of a radio-controlled toy car moving along a straight track, starting at rest at time = 0 seconds. The data table shows the position of the car in meters at one-second intervals. For each one-second interval (for example, the time between zero seconds and one second), calculate the *change* of position during that interval. This is the velocity, expressed in meters per second. Record your results in the velocity column in the data table. Do not make any entries in any of the dashed or shaded boxes. Note that you are actually calculating the *average* velocity for each time interval, since you don't know exact details of what happened within that interval.

2. You now have a list of velocities for several intervals. For each interval between velocity entries, find the *change* in velocity during that interval. This is the acceleration. Record your results in the acceleration column in the data table. Again, do not make any entries in any of the dashed or shaded boxes.

(continued)

Velocity and Acceleration *(continued)*

3. Assume that the last acceleration value you calculated stays constant for one additional second. (This is the value in the box across from the Time=6 seconds.) Copy this value into the shaded box in the Acceleration column. Using this value—together with the last velocity you found (the velocity between six and seven seconds)—find the average velocity between Time=7 seconds and Time=8 seconds. Enter this value into the shaded box in the Velocity column. Similarly, find the position of the car at Time=8 seconds and enter this value into the shaded box in the Position column.

4. On a single piece of graph paper, plot position, velocity, and acceleration each as a function of time using all the data in the data table. Use a different color pencil for each graph. Plot your graph with time on the horizontal axis, with a range of 0 to 10 seconds. Let the vertical axis scale go from 0 to 100 units—which may be meters, meters per second, or m/s^2 as required.

DATA COLLECTION AND ANALYSIS

Time (seconds)	Position (meters)	Velocity (m/s)	Acceleration (m/s/s)
0	0	-------------------	-------------------
-------------------	-------------------		-------------------
1	1	-------------------	
-------------------	-------------------		-------------------
2	3	-------------------	
-------------------	-------------------		-------------------
3	7	-------------------	
-------------------	-------------------		-------------------
4	14	-------------------	
-------------------	-------------------		-------------------
5	26	-------------------	
-------------------	-------------------		-------------------
6	43	-------------------	
-------------------	-------------------		-------------------
7	66	-------------------	
-------------------	-------------------		-------------------
8		-------------------	-------------------

(continued)

Velocity and Acceleration *(continued)*

 CONCLUDING QUESTIONS

1. The car moving along a straight track is an example of motion in how many (one, two, or three) dimensions? _____

2. If the time interval between position measurements had been two seconds instead of one second, what would you have had to do to the change in position during each interval to get velocity in meters per second? _____

    _____

3. What is the final position of the car at Time=8 seconds? _____

    _____

4. Examine the graphs you made. Which varies most during the eight seconds: position, velocity, or acceleration? Why? _____

    _____

    _____

 EXTENSION The area under a graph of velocity versus time gives the total distance traveled. From your velocity graph in step 4, estimate the total distance traveled by the toy car from zero through eight seconds. To do this, notice that each square "box" on your velocity graph represents 1m/s times 1 second, or 1 meter, so you can get an approximate answer by counting the boxes under the velocity graph from Time = 0 to Time = 8. Compare your answer with the value at the bottom of the position column. _____

_____

〽 Follow-up Activities 〽

1. List all the items you can think of that cause acceleration (any change in velocity, either magnitude or direction) in an automobile. How about on a bicycle?

2. For this activity, you will calculate the average magnitude of certain accelerations over a time interval. In textbooks and science classes, acceleration is normally expressed in metric units, such as meters per second per second. Here, however, you will probably have a better appreciation for the values if you calculate them in **miles per hour per second.**

    (a) If an ocean liner, starting from rest, reaches its cruising speed of 40 miles per hour after one hour, what is the average acceleration during that time?

    (b) Car manufacturers often brag about how quickly their cars can reach high speeds. What is the average acceleration of a car that can go from zero to 60 miles per hour in 10 seconds?

    (c) If the space shuttle reaches a speed of 2,000 miles per hour 20 seconds after launch, what is its average acceleration?

Newton's First Law: Inertia

 ## INSTRUCTIONAL OBJECTIVES

Students will be able to

- describe Newton's First Law of Motion.
- demonstrate the concept of inertia.
- draw conclusions based on data.

NATIONAL SCIENCE STANDARDS ADDRESSED

Students demonstrate an understanding of

- properties of matter.
- motions and forces.
- inertia.
- relevant concepts to explain observed phenomena.

Students demonstrate scientific inquiry and problem-solving skills by

- framing questions.
- working individually and in teams to collect and share information and ideas.
- identifying problems; evaluating accuracy, design, and outcome.

Students demonstrate effective scientific communication by

- arguing from evidence and data.

 ## MATERIALS

- A hard, smooth, *very flat* surface, such as a pane of window glass or sheet of Plexiglas™, about $\frac{1}{2}$ to 1 meter wide
- Table, bench, or countertop
- Assorted pieces of cardboard or paper of varying thickness
- Ping-pong ball, glass marble, or other hard, accurately spherical object
- Carpenter's bubble level
- Block of wood or hardcover book
- Erasable felt-tip marker

HELPFUL HINTS AND DISCUSSION

Time frame: 40 minutes, or a single period of instruction

Structure: Pairs (in class) or individuals (at home)

Location: In class or at home

Demonstrate the use of a bubble level. Explain how it works and why gravity has little or no influence on the motion of an object on a *level* horizontal surface. Also explain that a spherical object rolling on a flat surface behaves approximately as an object sliding on a frictionless surface. It is imperative that the surface be as flat as possible. Examine the surfaces that the students will be using to eliminate any warped or wavy ones. A left-handed student may exchange "left" and "right" in steps 2 through 5.

ADAPTATIONS FOR HIGH AND LOW ACHIEVERS

High Achievers: High achievers can be encouraged to do the Extension and the Follow-up Activity.

Low Achievers: Review with these students the relevant concepts, especially the definition of a force. These students can be paired with high achievers for the in-class activity.

SCORING RUBRIC

Full credit can be given to students who answer the questions correctly and in complete sentences. The quiz can be scored from 1 to 4 correct.

 ## INTERNET TIE-INS

http://www.glenbrook.k12.il.us/gbssci/phys/Class/newtlaws/newtltoc.html
http://www.execpc.com/~culp/space/newton.html
http://www.aloha.com/~isaac/3laws/

QUIZ

1. Define inertia.
2. What will happen to a spaceship moving in space when its rockets stop firing?
3. What is required for a stationary object to begin moving?
4. True or false: For an object to move in a straight line at a constant speed, it must be acted on by a force. Explain your answer.

Name _____   Date _____

Newton's First Law: Inertia

 BEFORE YOU BEGIN

In a bad science-fiction movie, you might see a spaceship flying through interstellar space, rocket engines blazing, and then coming to a halt when the rockets shut off. This might be good for the story line, but it's not the way the universe works.

The Italian Renaissance scientist Galileo Galilei figured out that if no forces act on an object, it will move at a constant velocity. For an object to change its velocity, some force or forces must act on the object. Therefore, the spaceship in the movie would continue to move at a constant speed and in a straight line after the engines shut down because in outer space there are no significant forces (aside from the weak gravity of distant stars or planets) to stop it. Additional force from the engines firing in the opposite direction would be needed to make the spaceship stop. Galileo's principle was incorporated by Isaac Newton into his First Law of Motion. The property of matter that makes objects maintain a constant velocity unless acted upon by an outside force is called **inertia**.

In this activity, you will examine motion in two dimensions for convenience, but your conclusions apply to three dimensions as well. You will also be using a rolling object instead of one which is simply moving in a straight line without rolling. This avoids difficulties (the effects of friction) that might hide the important principle being illustrated.

 MATERIALS

- A hard, smooth, *very flat* surface, such as a pane of window glass or sheet of Plexiglas™, about $\frac{1}{2}$ to 1 meter wide
- Table, bench, or countertop
- Assorted pieces of cardboard or paper of varying thickness

- Ping-pong ball, glass marble, or other hard, accurately spherical object
- Carpenter's bubble level
- Block of wood or hardcover book
- Erasable felt-tip marker

 PROCEDURE

1. You will need a flat, *level* surface so that gravity does not affect the motion being observed. Place the glass or other flat surface on a table. Using the bubble level, check to see that the surface is level. If not, place cardboard or wedges of paper as shims under the surface and recheck with the bubble level until the surface is as level as you can make it. Make sure to check and shim in two *perpendicular* directions, such as left/right and front/back, and recheck with the bubble level in both directions after any shims are changed.

2. Using the marker, mark the **middle of the right half of the flat surface** with a small *x*. After you have made certain that the surface is level, place the ball on the *x*. If you have done a good job in step 1, the ball should not roll. If it does, level the surface again. Repeat this process until the ball stays put when you place it on the flat surface.

(continued)

         Walch Hands-on Science Series: Force and Motion

Newton's First Law: Inertia *(continued)*

3. Rest the ball on the *x*. Observe what happens. Record your observations in the space indicated.

4. Hold the block in your hand, and use it to push the ball slowly to the left at a constant speed. Move the ball just fast enough that it reaches the left edge of the surface in two to four seconds. Be careful to push the ball, not bump it. Observe and record what happens during this action. You should repeat this step a few times to get the right speed and to be certain of your observations.

5. Place the ball back on the *x* where it was at the beginning of step 3. Again, push the ball to the left with the block. But this time, when you have moved the ball about halfway to the left edge, suddenly *stop* pushing and hold the block still. Observe and record what happens to the ball *after* you stopped pushing it with the block. You should repeat this step a few times to be certain of your observations.

DATA COLLECTION AND ANALYSIS

What happened to the ball in step 3 after you placed it in the middle of the right half of the flat surface? _____

_____

_____

Describe what happened in step 4 when you pushed the ball with the block. _____

_____

_____

_____

Describe what happened in step 5 when you stopped pushing the ball. _____

_____

_____

_____

EXTENSION Why do you think that the concept of Newton's First Law (inertia) is not obvious to someone in everyday life? (It was not obvious to ancient philosophers, like Aristotle, either.) What do we need to take into account when interpreting observations of moving objects that we haven't even mentioned here? (**Hint:** What are we trying to eliminate with our careful experimental setup?)

(continued)

Newton's First Law: Inertia *(continued)*

? CONCLUDING QUESTIONS

1. In step 3, did the velocity of the ball change? Did it obey Newton's First Law of Motion? What was missing that would have made it move? _____

   _____

   _____

   _____

2. In step 4, what was the initial speed of the ball? Did this speed change during step 4? What must have been present for this to happen? _____

   _____

   _____

   _____

3. In step 5, at what point did the force on the ball disappear? Immediately after the force disappeared, did the ball stop moving? Why or why not? _____

   _____

   _____

   _____

4. Why doesn't this work so easily in the real world? What are some factors that complicate the real-world experiment and cause the results to deviate (only slightly, we hope) from perfectly illustrating Newton's First Law? _____

   _____

   _____

   _____

   _____

⤜ Follow-up Activity ⤛

Repeat this exercise on a flat surface that is *not* smooth, such as a low carpet. How do your results differ from the experiment above. Why do you think they differ?

Newton's Second Law: The Effect of Force

 INSTRUCTIONAL OBJECTIVES

Students will be able to
- describe Newton's Seond Law of Motion.
- demonstrate the effects of mass and force on accelertion.
- record data in a table.
- draw conclusions based on data.

 NATIONAL SCIENCE STANDARDS ADDRESSED

Students demonstrate an understanding of
- motions and forces.
- inertia.
- relevant concepts to explain observed phenomena.

Students demonstrate scientific inquiry and problem-solving skills by
- using relevant concepts to explain observations and phenomena.
- identifying and controlling variables in experimental settings.
- using technology and tools to observe and measure objects.
- identifying problems; evaluating accuracy, design, and outcome.
- analyzing data using mathematical concepts, such as the mean.
- working in teams to collect and share information and ideas.

Students demonstrate effective scientific communication by
- arguing from evidence and data.
- representing data in multiple ways, such as numbers, tables, and graphs (extension activity).

 MATERIALS
- About 20 pennies
- Pencil
- Two wooden or strong plastic 12-inch rulers (one may be a meterstick)
- Transparent tape or white glue
- Jar, box, or other object 15 to 20 cm tall
- Table or bench
- Calculator (optional)
- Graph paper (extension activity)

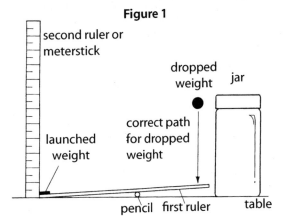

Figure 1

HELPFUL HINTS AND DISCUSSION

Time frame: 40 minutes, or a single period of instruction

Structure: Pairs

Location: In class or at home

Since it is difficult to measure acceleration without special equipment, this activity uses an indirect approach. A coin is launched upward by the impact of a weight dropped from a standard height. The height reached by the coin depends on its initial upward speed. This initial upward speed depends on the acceleration provided by the ruler, which depends on the coin's mass and on the force exerted by the weight dropped onto the raised end of the ruler. Good results require practice and care in dropping the weight consistently from the same height and onto the same spot on the ruler. The ruler/pencil seesaw converts the downward motion of the dropped weight into upward motion. Taping the packs of pennies together is acceptable, but gluing is preferred. Preparing these packs the day before the activity will allow the glue time to dry. Packs of pennies glued with white glue can be separated by soaking them in water overnight.

ADAPTATIONS FOR HIGH AND LOW ACHIEVERS

High Achievers: These students should be encouraged to do the Extensions and the Follow-up Activity.

Low Achievers: Review with these students the concepts involved in Newton's Second Law. Make sure they understand that they will be evaluating the acceleration and force indirectly by observing the maximum height of the launched weights.

SCORING RUBRIC

Full credit can be given to students whose data recorded in the Data Collection and Analysis section look reasonable and who answer the questions correctly and in complete sentences. The quiz can be scored from 1 to 4 correct.

 **INTERNET TIE-INS**   http://www.glenbrook.k12.il.us/gbssci/phys/Class/newtlaws/newtltoc.html
http://www.execpc.com/~culp/space/newton.html
http://www.aloha.com/~isaac/3laws/

 QUIZ   1. In what direction is force exerted on the launched penny?
2. What is the relationship between the force applied to an object and that object's acceleration?
3. For a specific amount of applied force, what would happen to an object's acceleration if its mass were increased?
4. To double the acceleration of an object, what must you do to the force applied to it?

Newton's Second Law: The Effect of Force

 BEFORE YOU BEGIN

Newton's First Law of Motion states that an object will change its velocity only when acted on by a force, but it doesn't say anything about how *much* the velocity will change. A certain force exerted on a baseball will have a much bigger effect than that same force will have on an apartment house. Based on ordinary experience, the Greek philosopher Aristotle incorrectly believed that the *velocity* of an object is proportional to the force applied to it. He failed to understand or account for the effects of friction. Based on work done by Galileo, Newton discovered that the **acceleration** (**A**) of an object is proportional to the **force** (**F**) applied to it and inversely proportional to the object's **mass** (M). As an equation, this is expressed

$$A = \frac{F}{M}$$

Note that force and acceleration are each vector quantities having both magnitude and direction, while mass is a scalar, which has only magnitude. Force is measured in **newtons** (N).

The importance of this little equation is enormous. It can be used to predict accurately the motion of a planet around the sun, a car on the highway, or a basketball on its way to the hoop. In this activity, you will see some of the practical implications of Newton's Second Law of Motion. Because it is very difficult to measure acceleration directly without special equipment, you will observe acceleration *indirectly*. In this activity, the maximum height reached by coins launched by a falling weight will serve as an indicator of acceleration.

 MATERIALS

- About 20 pennies
- Pencil
- Two wooden or strong plastic 12-inch rulers (one may be a meterstick)
- Transparent tape or white glue

- Jar, box, or other object 15 to 20 cm tall
- Table or bench
- Calculator (optional)
- Graph paper (extension activity)

 PROCEDURE

1. Prepare three packs of pennies for the experiment as follows: Using glue or tape to join the pennies, make a pack with two pennies, a pack with three pennies, and a pack with five pennies. If this step is done the day before the main activity, use a drop of white glue between the pennies. If this step is done during the main activity, use transparent tape—as little as possible— to hold the pennies together in a pack.

2. Prepare the launcher. Set the pencil on the table, and place the 12-inch ruler on top of and perpendicular to the pencil, with the pencil at the 7-inch mark of the ruler. The end of the long side of the ruler should be resting on the table, and the other end should be raised. Set the jar near the raised end; the top of the jar will be used as a standard height from which to drop a pack of pennies onto the raised end. Prop up or tape the second ruler or meterstick to stand *vertically* behind and near the end of the long side of the first ruler. The second ruler will be used to estimate the height reached by the launched packs. Have your partner positioned to see both the meterstick and the launched coins. Position yourself so that you can release the dropped pack onto the raised end of the ruler correctly and consistently. See Figure 1.

(continued)

Newton's Second Law: The Effect of Force *(continued)*

Figure 1

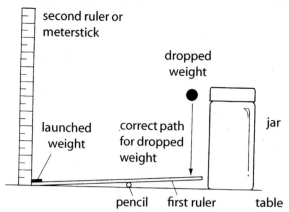

second ruler or meterstick

dropped weight

launched weight

correct path for dropped weight

jar

pencil　　first ruler　　table

3. Place a single penny on the end of the long side of the ruler resting on the table. Hold the two-penny pack directly above the raised end of the ruler at the height of the top of the jar, and drop the weight. The single penny will be "launched" upward. Have your partner estimate the height it reaches. Practice dropping and observing until you get consistent results each time. Be sure to reset the pencil on the table to the 7-inch mark of the ruler each time if needed. Then perform the experiment three times, recording the height reached by the single penny in the space provided in the Data Collection and Analysis section. Calculate and enter the average of the three trials.

4. Repeat step 3 using the five-penny pack as the dropped object and the single penny as the launched object.

5. Repeat step 3 with the five-penny pack as the dropped object and the three-penny pack as the launched object.

EXTENSION Repeat step 3, launching the single penny with the pack of three pennies. Record your results in the Data Collection and Analysis section. Now make a pack with four pennies. Repeat step 3, launching the single penny with the pack of four pennies. Record your results in the Data Collection and Analysis section. You have now launched the single penny with two, three, four, and five pennies. Make a table of your results. Using the data in your table, make a graph of height reached (on the *y*-axis) against force applied (on the *x*-axis). Explain your result.

DATA COLLECTION AND ANALYSIS

Record your observations below.

Dropped	Launched	Height Reached			
		Trial 1	Trial 2	Trial 3	Average
2 pennies	1 penny	_____cm	_____cm	_____cm	_____cm
5 pennies	1 penny	_____cm	_____cm	_____cm	_____cm
5 pennies	3 pennies	_____cm	_____cm	_____cm	_____cm

(continued)

Newton's Second Law: The Effect of Force *(continued)*

EXTENSION

Dropped	Launched	Height Reached			
		Trial 1	Trial 2	Trial 3	Average
3 pennies	1 penny	_____cm	_____cm	_____cm	_____cm
4 pennies	1 penny	_____cm	_____cm	_____cm	_____cm

CONCLUDING QUESTIONS

When answering the questions, assume

- that the height reached by the launched penny or pack is proportional to the acceleration it was given.
- that the mass of a launched pack is proportional to the number of pennies it contains.
- that the force applied to the launched pack is proportional to the number of pennies in the pack dropped from the standard height.

1. How does the acceleration of the launched pack depend on the force applied to it?

   _____

   _____

   _____

2. How does the acceleration of the launched pack depend on its own mass?

   _____

   _____

   _____

3. The third assumption above is itself an expression of Newton's Second Law. Explain.

   _____

   _____

   _____

Follow-up Activity

You can see the effect of Newton's Second Law in everyday life—for example, when riding a bicycle. To illustrate the dependence of acceleration on mass, think up an experiment using a bicycle, a backpack loaded with varying heavy weights, and a stopwatch. Write up the experiment so that others can try it.

Pressure Is Not the Same As Force

 INSTRUCTIONAL OBJECTIVES

Students will be able to
- describe the difference between pressure and force.
- demonstrate that increasing the area over which a force acts reduces the pressure.

 NATIONAL SCIENCE STANDARDS ADDRESSED

Students demonstrate an understanding of
- motions and forces.

Students demonstrate scientific inquiry and problem-solving skills by
- using relevant concepts to explain observations and phenomena.
- identifying and controlling variables in experimental settings.
- working in teams to collect and share information and ideas.

Students demonstrate effective scientific communication by
- arguing from evidence and data.

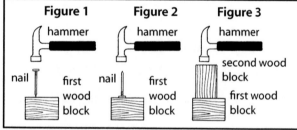

HELPFUL HINTS AND DISCUSSION

Time frame: 40 minutes, or a single period of instruction

Structure: Part A: Pairs, Part B: Individuals

Location: In class or at home

This activity involves subjective observation rather than quantitative measurement, so encourage all students to be careful and patient. For Part A, make sure that each pair of students has a sufficient quantity of plastic peanuts and that a single peanut crushes easily—if not, then find a different kind that does. Also, check the layer of peanuts that each pair of students makes to be sure that it contains as many peanuts as possible in a single layer the size of the board. If placed correctly, the peanuts should be able to support at least 300 pounds in step 4. Part B, whether done at home or in class, should be done only under adult supervision. Although the students are instructed not to hammer the nail all the way through the wood block, you may want to put a piece of scrap wood or other material under the block to protect the surface below.

 **MATERIALS**

PART A

For each pair:
- A wooden board at least 50 cm × 50 cm and about 2 cm thick
- Foam plastic "peanuts," the kind used for packing items for shipment

PART B

For each student:
- Two blocks of soft wood (e.g., pine), such as short sections of a two-by-four
- Hammer
- Two medium-size common nails (the kind with a wide head and length about 10 to 20 cm)
- Safety glasses

ADAPTATIONS FOR HIGH AND LOW ACHIEVERS	SCORING RUBRIC
High Achievers: These students should be encouraged to do the Extension and the Follow-up Activity. **Low Achievers:** Review the concepts of pressure and force with these students. Low achievers can be paired with high achievers for Part A of this activity.	Full credit can be given to students who answer the questions correctly and in complete sentences. The quiz can be scored from 1 to 4 correct.

 INTERNET TIE-INS   http://ldaps.ivv.nasa.gov/Curriculum/Curriculum/Force-vs.-Pressure.html

 **QUIZ**
1. What is the difference between force and pressure?
2. If you know the force being exerted, what else do you need to know to determine the pressure?
3. In what kind of situation or problem is force the relevant factor?
4. In what kind of situation or problem is pressure the relevant factor?

Name _____   Date _____

Pressure Is Not the Same As Force

BEFORE YOU BEGIN

How can a magician lie on a bed of nails without apparent harm? Why do snowshoes allow you to walk across the surface of the snow without sinking? The answer to these questions involves the difference between force and pressure. A common misunderstanding is that force and pressure are the same thing, but they are not. For example, saying "The stuck door finally opened when I put more pressure on it with my shoulder" would be incorrect, even though most people would understand what you meant.

Pressure is force exerted **per unit of area**. If you have a certain force, say 1 newton, and apply it to an object over a contact area of 1 square meter, then the pressure over this area is 1 newton per square meter (N/m^2). If the same force were applied over only 0.1 square meter, the pressure would be 1 newton divided by 0.1 square meter, or $10\ N/m^2$. Pressure can be found by dividing the total force exerted by the total area over which it acts. On the other hand, if you know the pressure, you can calculate the total force by multiplying that pressure by total area affected.

Whether you need to be concerned with force or with pressure depends on the situation or problem you are considering. If you are concerned with the motion of whole objects as they interact, then you need to know about the forces involved. If you need to know about damage to or changes in the shape or size of an object, then you probably are concerned with the pressure. In the case of the stuck door, what really matters is the *force* you exert on the door with your shoulder, since this force must overcome the friction that is keeping the door closed.

MATERIALS

PART A

For each pair:

- A wooden board at least 50 cm × 50 cm and about 2 cm thick
- Foam plastic "peanuts," the kind used for packing items for shipment

PART B

For each student:

- Two blocks of soft wood (e.g., pine), such as short sections of a two-by-four
- Hammer
- Two medium-size common nails (the kind with a wide head and length about 10 to 20 cm)
- Safety glasses

PROCEDURE

PART A

 **Do steps 3–4 only with adult supervision.**

1. Pick a single undamaged peanut. Place it on the floor. Step on it, placing your full weight on that foot. Remove your foot, and observe and record the condition of the peanut in the Data Collection and Analysis section.

2. Spread the remaining peanuts on the floor. Make a layer one peanut thick over an area about the size and shape of the wooden board. Use your hand to pat down and even out the layer. Try to get as many peanuts into the area as you can.

(continued)

Pressure Is Not the Same As Force *(continued)*

3. Slowly and carefully, lower the board onto the layer of peanuts. Check to see if the board rocks over a high point in the layer of peanuts. If it does, remove the board, level the peanuts again, and replace the board. At the end of this step, the board should be level and steady when resting on the layer of peanuts.

4. Stand on the board in the following manner: Carefully place one foot on the board near its *center*, and then step on with the other foot, also near the center of the board. Be careful not to step near the edges of the board, or your weight will be distributed unevenly. Stand still on the board for several seconds, and then carefully step off. *Slowly* and carefully remove the board, and inspect the peanuts that were under it. Observe and record their condition in the Data Collection and Analysis section.

PART B

> Do this only under the strict supervision of an adult.

1. Put on the safety glasses. Place one block of wood (the larger, if they are not of equal size) on a secure surface, such as the floor or a workbench.

2. Try to hammer one of the nails into the block of wood with the pointed end of the nail toward the wood. If you succeed, hammer only a few strokes. **Do not hammer the nail through to the other side of the wood block.** Observe and record the result, including the condition of the block of wood, in the Data Collection and Analysis section. See Figure 1.

3. Try to hammer the other nail into the block of wood, this time with the *flat* end of the nail toward the wood. Try to use the **same force** with the hammer that you used in step 2. Do **not** hammer harder if you do not succeed at first. If you do succeed, hammer only a few strokes. **Do not hammer the nail through to the other side of the wood block.** Observe and record the result, including the condition of the block of wood, in the Data Collection and Analysis section. See Figure 2.

4. Try to hammer the second block of wood into the larger one, placing a flat end (not a corner or edge) of the second block against the first block. Try to use the **same force** as you used in step 2. Do **not** hammer harder if you do not succeed at first. Observe and record the result, including the condition of the first block of wood. See Figure 3.

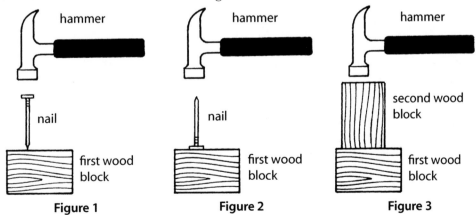

Figure 1   Figure 2   Figure 3

(continued)

Pressure Is Not the Same As Force *(continued)*

DATA COLLECTION AND ANALYSIS

PART A

Condition of the plastic peanut after step 1 _____

Condition of the plastic peanuts after step 4 _____

PART B

Nail, pointed end down _____

Nail, flat end down _____

Block of wood _____

CONCLUDING QUESTIONS

PART A

1. Did the single foam peanut support your weight? What happened to the single peanut, and why?

   _____

   _____

   _____

2. Did the layer of peanuts support your weight? Were any of the peanuts in the same condition as the single peanut? Why or why not? _____

   _____

   _____

3. Was the total force on the single peanut greater than the total force on the entire layer

   of peanuts? _____

PART B

1. Which object was easiest to hammer into the first block of wood? Why? _____

   _____

   _____

   _____

2. If any object could not be hammered into the first block of wood, was any other effect on the

   wood noticeable? _____

   _____

   _____

(continued)

Pressure Is Not the Same As Force *(continued)*

⟿ EXTENSION

Repeat Part A of this experiment with materials other than plastic peanuts and weights other than yourself. Can you draw any conclusions about what factors are important in supporting heavy objects? _____

_____

_____

 Follow-up Activity

There are many objects at home and at school that, by their design, either concentrate weight or some other force in a small contact area, producing a high pressure. Others spread the force out over a large area, making the pressure relatively low. Identify and make two lists of at least 10 such objects: one list for those that concentrate the force and one for those that spread it out.

Newton's Third Law: Action and Reaction

 ## INSTRUCTIONAL OBJECTIVES

Students will be able to

- explain Newton's Third Law of Motion.
- demonstrate the concepts of action and reaction.

 ## NATIONAL SCIENCE STANDARDS ADDRESSED

Students demonstrate an understanding of

- properties of matter.
- motions and forces; fundamental laws of nature.
- relevant concepts to explain observed phenomena.

Students demonstrate scientific inquiry and problem-solving skills by

- framing questions.
- working in teams to collect and share information and ideas
- identifying problems; evaluating accuracy, design, and outcome.

Students demonstrate effective scientific communication by

- arguing from evidence and data.
- writing instructions others can follow (extension activity).

 ## MATERIALS

For each group:

- Bathroom scale
- About 100 pounds of gym weights in various sizes, or similar
- Low stepstool, sturdy chair, or wooden box, such as a milk crate
- Handheld mirror
- A strong, flat board, approximately the size of the bathroom scale

  For the Extension:

- Strong string or cord
- Pulleys
- Two spring scales
- Sheet of lined paper

HELPFUL HINTS AND DISCUSSION

Time frame: 40 minutes, or a single period of instruction
Structure: Pairs of students
Location: In class or at home

If a chair is used in this exercise, try to find one with a flat, hard, level seat. Some bathroom scales may not work properly upside down; if a student encounters this problem, give the student access to a scale that functions in an inverted position. Some digital scales require a minimum weight to initiate a reading, so test the scale for this and be sure all objects weighed exceed this minimum weight. The total weight should be about 50 to 100 pounds.

ADAPTATIONS FOR HIGH AND LOW ACHIEVERS

High Achievers: These students should be encouraged to do the Extension and Follow-up Activities.

Low Achievers: Review the relevant concepts and procedures, especially the concept of force, with these students prior to having them carry out this activity. They can be grouped with high achievers for the in-class activity.

SCORING RUBRIC

Full credit can be given to students who answer the questions correctly and in complete sentences. The quiz can be scored from 1 to 4 correct.

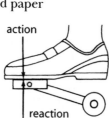

INTERNET TIE-INS
http://www.glenbrook.k12.il.us/gbssci/phys/Class/newtlaws/newtltoc.html
http://www.execpc.com/~culp/space/newton.html
http://www.aloha.com/~isaac/3laws/

 **QUIZ**

1. Consider an action consisting of the force exerted by your hand on a door. What is the *reaction*?

2. An elephant and a mouse play tug-of-war. Is the force exerted by the mouse on the elephant less than, equal to, or greater than the force exerted by the elephant on the mouse?

3. True or false: If you push on a chair, Newton's Third Law states that the chair pushes back on you with equal and opposite force, so *neither you nor the chair can move*. Explain your answer.

4. A rocket engine exerts a force on the expanding gases inside it, pushing them out the nozzle. What, if anything, exerts a force on the rocket engine?

Name _____ Date _____

Newton's Third Law: Action and Reaction

 BEFORE YOU BEGIN

When you push on the pedal of a bicycle, you feel a force on the bottom of your foot. When you lift your foot off the pedal, the sensation of force is eliminated. Why?

The answer lies in Newton's Third Law of Motion, which states that **for every action there is an equal and opposite reaction**. To be more specific, when two objects physically interact, the **force** exerted by the second object on the first (the reaction) must be equal to the force exerted by the first object on the second (the action), but it points in the *opposite* direction. When your foot (the first object) is pushing *down* on the pedal (the second object), the pedal is also pushing *up* on your foot with exactly the same magnitude of force, as shown in Figure 1. This is true whether the bicycle is at rest, moving at a constant speed, or accelerating—as long as the pedal and your foot are in contact. We encounter Newton's Third Law constantly in ordinary life when walking, playing, or even sitting. (What is exerting a force on what?)

This law is sometimes confused with the fact that when all forces on a single object are "balanced" (sum to zero), the object experiences no acceleration. Strictly speaking, Newton's Third Law doesn't say *anything* about how or whether either of the two bodies moves. That depends only on the sum of all the forces on each object independently, along with Newton's First and Second Laws.

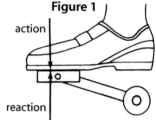

Figure 1

action

reaction

In this activity, you will show that the forces involved really are equal and oppositely directed. For the purpose of this exercise, we will think of the bathroom scale as measuring the force (weight) exerted *by* the object in contact with its top surface on the object in contact with its bottom surface.

MATERIALS

For each group:

- Bathroom scale
- About 100 pounds of gym weights in various sizes
- Low stepstool, sturdy chair, or wooden box, such as a milk crate
- Handheld mirror

- A strong, flat board, approximately the size of the bathroom scale

For the Extension:
- Strong string or cord
- Pulleys
- Two spring scales
- Sheet of lined paper

PROCEDURE

1. Place the stepstool on a hard (uncarpeted) floor. Place the scale flat and right-side up on the stepstool. Do not place anything on the scale. If the bathroom scale has a zero-point adjustment feature, make this adjustment now.

2. Place the flat board on the scale. This will serve to distribute the weight evenly in a later step, so it must be included in your first measurement as well. Place the gym weights on the board, and ask your partner to read the combined weight of the gym weights and the board. Record this weight in the space provided. This weight represents the force exerted *downward* on the stepstool.

(continued)

Newton's Third Law: Action and Reaction *(continued)*

3. Remove the scale and board from the stepstool. Place the scale *upside down* on the stepstool, and place the board on the bottom surface of the scale, which is now facing upward. Place the mirror on the floor so that you can read the scale without crouching under it—this may take some practice. Place the same gym weights as in step 2 on the board, and have your partner read the combined weight and record it in the space provided. This weight represents the force exerted *upward* on the weights.

4. Repeat the measurements in steps 2 and 3, weighing another combination of gym weights with a different total weight.

DATA COLLECTION AND ANALYSIS

Force exerted by the weights on the stepstool: _____ lbs.

Force exerted by the stepstool on the weights: _____ lbs.

Force exerted by another combination of weights on the stepstool: _____ lbs.

Force exerted by the stepstool on another combination of weights: _____ lbs.

CONCLUDING QUESTIONS

1. Within the accuracy of the scale, typically a pound or so, does the *magnitude* of the force exerted by the stepstool equal the force exerted by the weights? If not, what do you think is happening?

   _____

   _____

   _____

   _____

2. How does the *direction* of the force exerted by the stepstool compare with the direction of the force exerted by the weights? _____

   _____

   _____

3. From your observations, does the validity of Newton's Third Law depend on the magnitude of the force measured? Explain your answer. _____

   _____

   _____

   _____

   _____

(continued)

Newton's Third Law: Action and Reaction *(continued)*

 EXTENSION

A very convincing demonstration of Newton's Third Law can be made using strong string or cord, weights, pulleys, and two spring scales. Devise such an experiment, and on a separate sheet of paper, write clear instructions so that others in your class can carry it out.

🐾 Follow-up Activities 🐾

1. Look for and describe in writing three additional examples of Newton's Third Law of Motion in everyday life. You might not immediately recognize many of these for what they are, because forces in several directions and from several sources are usually involved, so look for simple situations.

2. Describe the motion of a rocket in space in terms of Newton's Third Law.

Friction

 ## INSTRUCTIONAL OBJECTIVES

Students will be able to

- describe and demonstrate static and kinetic friction.
- describe and demonstrate factors that influence friction.

 ## NATIONAL SCIENCE STANDARDS ADDRESSED

Students demonstrate an understanding of

- net forces.
- friction.

Students demonstrate scientific inquiry and problem-solving skills by

- framing questions.
- identifying and controlling variables.

Students demonstrate effective scientific communication by

- representing data in multiple ways.
- arguing from evidence and data.

MATERIALS

- Empty plastic margarine tub or similar
- Empty plastic 35-mm film canister or similar
- Lightweight string or thread about 75 cm long
- 50 to 100 pennies
- Tape (vinyl electrical tape preferred; clean plastic tape OK)
- Table, counter, or bench with a smooth surface
- Smooth, uncrumpled sheet of newspaper
- Sheet of sandpaper, $8\frac{1}{2}" \times 11"$

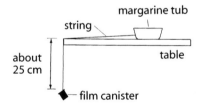

HELPFUL HINTS AND DISCUSSION

Time frame: 40 minutes, or a single period of instruction
Structure: Groups of two or three students
Location: In class

Make sure the students understand that the forces between the margarine tub and film canister are to be *just* balanced. When they are just balanced, the margarine tub might slide a little and then stop. It should be easy to get it sliding again if you give it a little push. If the tub moves easily in step 2, the student should remove the most recently added penny to achieve a reasonable balance. Have the students experiment with this concept of balance. Although the materials for this activity may be readily available at home, a teacher's assistance and suggestions will be helpful in obtaining good results. Encourage all students to practice before recording their results.

ADAPTATIONS FOR HIGH AND LOW ACHIEVERS

High Achievers: Encourage these students to do the Extension and the Follow-Up Activities. If they work in class, provide them with various other surfaces with which to experiment. These students may do the activity at home, if desired.

Low Achievers: Review the concept of balance between forces, as above. Have reference books available that describe the relevant concepts.

SCORING RUBRIC

Full credit can be given to students who carry out the procedure and answer the questions correctly and in complete sentences. The quiz can be scored from 1 to 3 correct.

INTERNET TIE-INS   http://www.drury.edu/education/fred/activities/friction/friction.html
http://zebu.uoregon.edu/1995/ph161/friction.html

 **QUIZ**   1. Distinguish between kinetic friction and static friction.
2. Why can't a machine, such as a motor, ever be 100 percent efficient?
3. True or false: The direction of the frictional force on an object is always the same as the direction of the actual motion of an object.

Friction

  BEFORE YOU BEGIN

You're riding a bicycle on level ground, and then you stop pedaling. If you apply the brake, you slow down. Even if you don't apply the brake, you still slow down, but less quickly. In either case, the force slowing you down is **friction**. Friction is a force that *always* opposes motion. Friction that occurs as two objects in contact slide past each other (like your bicycle wheel and the brake pad) is called **kinetic friction**. The amount of friction depends on the kinds of surfaces that are in contact, but some friction is always present. Some of the force produced by a machine's motor is always "wasted" on overcoming friction between its parts. Machines use lubricants (oil, Teflon™, etc.) or bearings to reduce friction so that they can operate more efficiently. Of course, sometimes friction is desirable, as when you apply your bicycle brake.

Friction that prevents two objects from sliding past each other is called **static friction**. A good example of static friction occurs between your bicycle tire and the road. The tire and road are designed to have a large frictional force between them, so that while the bicycle is moving, the part of the tire in contact with the road is not. If this frictional force were made very small, the wheel would slip on the road and the bicycle would not move forward. In this activity, you will experiment with static friction.

The **magnitude** of the frictional force is proportional to the magnitude of the force holding the two objects together (called the **normal force**). It also depends on the materials and detailed microscopic structure of the two surfaces in contact. The frictional force always acts in a direction opposing any motion. The direction of kinetic friction is opposite the object's velocity. The direction of static friction is opposite that of the force trying to move the object.

 MATERIALS

- Empty plastic margarine tub or similar container
- Empty plastic 35-mm film canister
- Lightweight string or thread about 75 cm long
- 50 to 100 pennies

- Tape (vinyl electrical tape preferred; clean plastic tape OK)
- Table, counter, or bench with a smooth surface
- Smooth, uncrumpled sheet of newspaper
- Sheet of sandpaper, $8\frac{1}{2}" \times 11"$

 PROCEDURE

1. Tape one end of the string to the side of the film canister so that the canister can be suspended by the string without spilling its contents. Tape the other end of the string to the side of the margarine tub, near the bottom. With both containers empty, place the margarine tub on the table with the film canister hanging over the edge by about 25 cm. We will call this position "home." See the diagram to the right.

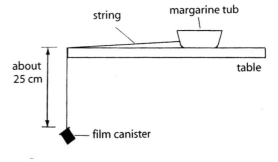

(continued)

Friction *(continued)*

2. You need to start by balancing the frictional force between the empty margarine tub and the surface it is sitting on against the force of gravity exerted on the empty film canister (and, through the string, on the margarine tub). Place the tub "home." Then, with the string taut, let go of the film canister. If the tub moves toward the edge of the table, put a penny in it, place it back home, and try again. If the tub does not move, put a penny in the film canister, place it back home, and try again. Repeat this test, adding pennies until the tub just barely holds its position on the table. Record the number of pennies in each container in the Data Collection and Analysis table.

3. Return the margarine tub to home, and add 20 pennies to it. This increases the normal force between the bottom of the tub and the table. Now add pennies to the film canister until the tub just begins to slide toward the edge of the table. Remove one penny from the film canister so that again the tub just barely holds its position on the table. Record the number of pennies in each container in the Data Collection and Analysis table.

4. Remove all the pennies from both containers. Tape the sandpaper to the table over the home position, sand side up. Return the tub to home. Repeat steps 2 and 3, and record your results in the section of the table marked "Sandpaper."

5. Replace the sandpaper with a single sheet of newspaper. Return the tub to home, repeat steps 2 and 3, and record your results.

6. When the forces are balanced in steps 2 and 3, the weight of the film canister (measured in pennies) is equal to the force of friction between the margarine tub and the table, and the weight of the margarine tub is equal to the normal force. For each of the three surfaces, you increased the normal force by the same amount by adding 20 pennies to the margarine tub. The number of pennies added to the film canister between steps 2 and 3 measures the added frictional force caused by the increased normal force. Calculate and record the *increase* in the number of pennies in the film canister for each surface.

(continued)

Friction *(continued)*

 DATA COLLECTION AND ANALYSIS

Surface	Step	# of pennies in margarine tub	# of pennies in film canister
Bare table	2		
	3		
	increase (step 3 minus step 2)	20	
Sandpaper	2		
	3		
	increase (step 3 minus step 2)	20	
Newspaper	2		
	3		
	increase (step 3 minus step 2)	20	

EXTENSION

Repeat the measurement of the force of static friction for table surfaces other than those described in steps 2 through 5. Also, try the experiment with various materials attached to the bottom of the margarine tub. Finally, try using the same material for both the margarine tub and table surface. What conclusions can you draw?

CONCLUDING QUESTIONS

1. What is the direction of the force produced on the margarine tub by the string? What is the direction of the force of friction between the margarine tub and the table surface? When the margarine tub is balanced in step 2, what must be true about the magnitude of these forces?

_____

_____

_____

_____

(continued)

Friction *(continued)*

2. In step 3, what does the addition of 20 pennies to the margarine tub do to the magnitude of the normal force between the tub and the table surface? What does this do to the force of friction? What must you do to the film canister to get the tub to move? _____

_____

_____

_____

_____

3. From your results in the bold-outlined boxes (on page 41), which surface produces the most friction? Which produces the least?

_____

_____

_____

_____

4. Some of the error in this activity comes from a source of friction other than that between the bottom of the margarine tub and the surface it sits on. Find and describe this source of friction, and suggest a way to reduce it. _____

_____

_____

_____

⤜ Follow-up Activities ⤜

1. This activity measures static friction. Think up and describe an experiment to measure the force of *kinetic* friction, the friction between two *moving* objects, using just a spring scale, a flat surface, and an object of known weight. If you have access to these materials, try the experiment!

2. List as many parts of a car as you can that are intended to reduce friction. List those that use friction in order to work. Look carefully and think about the function of each part—you may find some surprises.

Center of Mass

 ## INSTRUCTIONAL OBJECTIVES

Students will be able to
- describe what the center of mass of an object is.
- demonstrate a method of finding the center of gravity.
- draw conclusions based on data.

 ## NATIONAL SCIENCE STANDARDS ADDRESSED

Students demonstrate an understanding of
- properties of matter.
- motions and forces.
- relevant concepts to explain observed phenomena.

Students demonstrate scientific inquiry and problem-solving skills by
- framing questions.
- identifying problems; evaluating accuracy, design, and outcome.

Students demonstrate effective scientific communication by
- arguing from evidence and data.

 ## MATERIALS

- Meterstick
- 30 pennies
- Sandwich-size plastic bag
- Scissors
- Smooth table, counter, or bench
- Pencil with rubber eraser
- Paperback book
- Sheet of paper
- Masking tape
- Pen (ballpoint or felt-tip)
- Graph paper (extension activity)

HELPFUL HINTS AND DISCUSSION

Time frame: 40 minutes, or a single period of instruction, including time for teaching concepts
Structure: Individuals
Location: In class or at home

This activity is very straightforward, and most students should encounter no difficulties.

ADAPTATIONS FOR HIGH AND LOW ACHIEVERS

High Achievers: Encourage these students to do the Extension and the Follow-Up Activities.

Low Achievers: Low achievers should review the relevant concepts, especially that gravity acts on all objects with the same downward acceleration. These students can be paired with high achievers if the activity is done in class.

SCORING RUBRIC

Full credit can be given to students who answer the questions correctly and in complete sentences. The quiz can be scored from 1 to 4 correct.

Figure 1
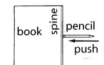

Figure 2
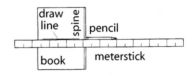

 ## INTERNET TIE-INS

http://www.exploratorium.edu/xref/phenomena/center_of_mass%252fgravity.html
http://www1.scasd.k12.pa.us/scasd/hs/departments/science/phys/hopkins/Chapt7Day9CentoMass.html

 ## QUIZ

1. Define the center of mass.
2. True or false: The force supporting a balanced seesaw is directed through its center of gravity.
3. What does an object do if the net force on it is not directed through its center of mass?
4. If you take a lump of material and attach it to an object, the object's center of mass will
   (a) move away from the newly added material.
   (b) move toward the newly added material.
   (c) stay where it was.

Center of Mass

 BEFORE YOU BEGIN

In other activities, we discuss forces acting on such objects as a bicycle pedal, a baseball, and a door, but *where* on each object do the forces act? If the object was extremely small, like an atom, we might not care. However, most everyday objects have a significant size and a shape that may be simple or complex, so on which part of the object can we think of the forces acting? To serve this purpose, we define an imaginary point called the **center of mass**—the average position of all the mass contained in an object. If any force on an object is directed through its center of mass, the object accelerates according to Newton's Laws of Motion—*without rotating*. If the force on the object is not directed through the center of mass, it will rotate as well as accelerate.

For an object with a simple symmetrical shape, like a sphere or cube, and uniform density (mass per unit volume), the center of mass is the same point as the geometrical center of the object. For a more complicated shape, we can calculate the center of mass if we know its density at every point (not easy!), or we can exert forces on the object and observe how it moves. This is simplest to understand if the force is uniform over the entire object.

Luckily, we have a force that acts on all parts of an object equally—gravity! Suppose we support the object against gravity at some point. If the object does not rotate (because the force of gravity is balanced on either side of the object), we know that the vector representing the force supporting the object goes through the center of mass. What we actually determine this way is called the **center of gravity**, which for ordinary purposes is the same as the center of mass.

 MATERIALS

- Meterstick
- 30 pennies
- Sandwich-size plastic bag
- Scissors

- Smooth table, counter, or bench
- Pencil with rubber eraser
- Paperback book
- Sheet of paper

- Masking tape
- Pen (ballpoint or felt-tip)
- Graph paper (extension activity)

 PROCEDURE

PART A

1. Hold the meterstick horizontal by supporting it near both ends from below with your index fingers. Be sure your index fingers are extended horizontally and are parallel to each other.

2. Slowly bring your index fingers together, allowing the meterstick to slide over the tops of your fingers and keeping the meterstick parallel to the floor. When your fingers meet, the meterstick should be nicely balanced at the center of mass of the meterstick. Note the position in cm on the meterstick where your fingers meet; record this value in the Data Collection and Analysis section.

3. Place 10 pennies in the plastic bag, and use the scissors to cut a hole 4 to 5 cm wide through both sides of the bag near the opening. Using this hole, hang the plastic bag on the 0-cm end of the meterstick. Repeat step 2, again recording the location of the center of mass on the meterstick in the Data Collection and Analysis section.

4. Repeat step 2 with 20 and then 30 pennies in the bag, and record your results.

(continued)

Center of Mass (continued)

PART B

1. Cut a rectangle from the sheet of paper the same size as the cover of the book, and tape it to the cover, face up.

2. Hold the writing end of the pencil, and place the pencil flat on the table. Placing the eraser end of the pencil against the spine of the book, try pushing the book across the table, as shown in Figure 1. Keep the pencil perpendicular to the spine of the book, and try pushing at various points on the spine (top, center, bottom, and points in between). Observe the motion of the book; record your observations in the Data Collection and Analysis section. Include direction of rotation, if any, in the space provided.

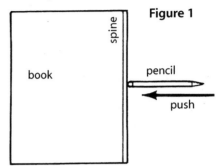

Figure 1

3. With a little practice, find the point on the spine that you can push to slide the book across the table without rotation. Let go of the pencil in that position. Using the meterstick as a straight edge, draw a line on the piece of paper you taped to the cover following the position and direction of the pencil. (See Figure 2.)

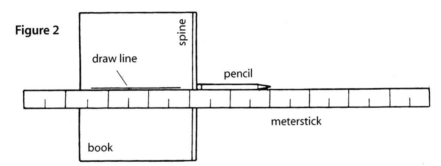

Figure 2

4. Repeat step 3, this time pushing on the bottom edge of the book rather than the spine. At the end of this step you should have drawn a large "X" on the book cover, designating the center of mass of the book.

DATA COLLECTION AND ANALYSIS

PART A

Center of mass of meterstick alone: _____ cm

Center of mass of meterstick + 10 pennies: _____ cm

Center of mass of meterstick + 20 pennies: _____ cm

Center of mass of meterstick + 30 pennies: _____ cm

(continued)

Center of Mass *(continued)*

EXTENSION Graph the location of the center of mass against the number of pennies in the bag, from 0 to 30. If you do not assume that the mass of the small plastic bag is negligible, how can you improve the experiment?

PART B

Motion of book pushing near top of the spine: _____

_____

Motion of book pushing near center of the spine: _____

_____

Motion of book pushing near bottom of the spine: _____

_____

CONCLUDING QUESTIONS

1. Was the center of mass of the meterstick near the center of the stick? _____

2. As you add mass to the end of the meterstick, what happens to the center of mass?

   _____

3. How does the book move when you direct the force of the pencil through the book's center of mass? What happens when you push near the top of the spine, and how does this differ from pushing on the bottom of the spine? _____

   _____

4. Does the center of gravity you found for the book appear to be at its geometrical center?

   _____

EXTENSION Where will the center of mass be if the total mass of the pennies greatly exceeds the mass of the meterstick? _____

_____

⚛ Follow-up Activities ⚛

1. The method of finding the center of gravity shown in Part A relies on both gravity and friction. Knowing this, explain how it works (**Hint:** Notice that your fingers do not move smoothly and simultaneously toward the center of gravity). Use the method in Part A to find the center of gravity of a variety of household objects. What can go wrong with this method?

2. Draw some two-dimensional shapes, and try to find the location of the center of mass of each by estimating its geometrical center. Draw a two-dimensional shape for which the center of mass is **not** within the object itself.

Earth's Gravity and Uniform Acceleration

 ## INSTRUCTIONAL OBJECTIVES

Students will be able to
- describe the acceleration due to Earth's gravity.
- demonstrate that the acceleration of gravity is independent of mass.
- record data in a table.
- draw conclusions based on data.

 ## NATIONAL SCIENCE STANDARDS ADDRESSED

Students demonstrate an understanding of
- motions and forces; gravity.
- relevant concepts to explain observed phenomena.

Students demonstrate scientific inquiry and problem-solving skills by
- framing questions to distinguish cause and effect.
- identifying and controlling variables in an experimental setting.

Students demonstrate effective scientific communication by
- arguing from evidence and data.

 ## MATERIALS

PART A
- A pillow, cushion, or other thick, soft surface to drop objects onto
- Two identical, small plastic bottles with caps that make a waterproof seal (e.g., empty liquid medicine bottles, hotel shampoo bottles, spice bottles)
- Modeling clay
- Triple-beam or other balance accurate to 0.1 gram
- Sheet of paper

PART B
- Pen or pencil

 ## INTERNET TIE-IN   http://www.phys.virginia.edu/classes/109N/1995/lectures/galaccn.html

HELPFUL HINTS AND DISCUSSION

Time frame: 40 minutes, or a single period of instruction
Structure: Individuals
Location: In class and/or at home

Much of this activity can be done at home, but prior to beginning the activity, students might be well advised to select and weigh their pieces of paper and weigh out the clay at school, where appropriate balances are available. Review the use of whatever balance is provided for the students' use. Remind the students to be careful to drop the objects on a soft surface.

ADAPTATIONS FOR HIGH AND LOW ACHIEVERS

High Achievers: Encourage these students to do the Extensions and the Follow-Up Activities.

Low Achievers: It would be helpful to review the concepts of and relationship between velocity and acceleration for these students. Make sure reference materials are available to them during the activity.

SCORING RUBRIC

Full credit can be given to students who answer the questions correctly and in complete sentences. The quiz can be scored from 1 to 4 correct.

QUIZ

1. Compare the rate of fall of a heavy object and a light one of the same size and shape.
2. Define uniform acceleration.
3. How does the distance traveled by a uniformly accelerated object starting from rest depend on time?
4. How does the distance traveled by a uniformly accelerated object starting from rest depend on its acceleration?

Earth's Gravity and Uniform Acceleration

> ### BEFORE YOU BEGIN
>
> The effects of Earth's gravity have, of course, been known throughout human history: Objects in general fall toward Earth, not away from it. Until the Renaissance it was widely believed that heavier objects fall faster than lighter ones. Galileo Galilei proved this was wrong with several careful experiments showing that the mass of a falling body does not affect its rate of fall. In this activity, you will reproduce one of these experiments in which he is supposed to have dropped different objects from the famous Leaning Tower in Pisa, Italy.
>
> Galileo also showed that the distance an object starting at rest falls is proportional to the square of the time since its release. This can be true only if the object is undergoing **uniform** (constant) acceleration. In uniform acceleration, the change in velocity is directly proportional to time. We usually identify the acceleration of gravity at the earth's surface as **g**, a vector with a magnitude of approximately 9.8 m/s^2 directed toward the center of the earth.
>
> The earth's gravity at its surface is the best known cause of constant acceleration in one dimension. The lessons we learn from it apply to other forces as well, even in complicated cases in which the effects of individual forces are not easily separated.

MATERIALS

PART A

- A pillow, cushion, or other thick, soft surface to drop objects onto
- Two identical, small plastic bottles with caps that make a waterproof seal (e.g., empty liquid medicine bottles, hotel shampoo bottles, spice bottles)
- Modeling clay
- Triple-beam or other balance accurate to 0.1 gram
- Sheet of paper

PART B
- Pen or pencil

PROCEDURE

PART A

1. Fill one of the plastic bottles with water and leave the other empty. You now have two objects with the same size and shape, but with different mass and density. Hold both objects at arm's length at the same height over the pillow. Drop them both simultaneously, and note the order in which they hit the pillow. It may take some practice to release both objects at the same time. Consider it a tie if you cannot distinguish two separate sounds as the objects hit.

2. Form some of the clay into two balls, one about 3 cm in diameter and the other about 1 cm in diameter. You now have two objects with the same density and shape, but different size and mass. Weigh the clay balls, and record these values in the space provided in the Data Collection and Analysis section. With these objects repeat the drop experiment, as in step 1.

3. Use the balance to find the mass of the sheet of paper. Record it for reference in the space provided in the Data Collection and Analysis section. Weigh out an equal mass of clay and form it into a ball. You now have two objects with the same mass, but different size, density, and shape. Starting with the sheet of paper horizontal, repeat the step 1 drop experiment with the paper and the equal-mass clay ball.

(continued)

Earth's Gravity and Uniform Acceleration *(continued)*

 EXTENSION

Repeat the drop experiment with other materials of different sizes and masses around the classroom or at home. (Make sure these materials are safe to drop.) Relate your observations to those in the exercise.

PART B

1. Data Table 1 represents the motion of an object that begins at rest at Time = 0 seconds and then starts to move with uniform acceleration. **Note: This is not an example of an object falling under Earth's gravity. Rather, it is a general example of accelerated motion.** The first column gives the time, the second column gives the position at that time, and the third column gives the velocity of the object during each time interval. Using the information provided, complete the table by filling in the correct values for Position and Velocity where they are not provided for you. Do not make any entries in the shaded areas.

DATA COLLECTION AND ANALYSIS

PART A

Check which object strikes the pillow first:

Empty bottle _____   Full bottle _____   Tie _____

Large ball _____   Small ball _____   Tie _____

Paper _____   Clay _____   Tie _____

Mass of the large ball: _____ grams

Mass of the small ball: _____ grams

Mass of the sheet of paper: _____ grams

(continued)

Earth's Gravity and Uniform Acceleration *(continued)*

PART B

Data Table 1

Time (seconds)	Position (meters)	Velocity (m/s)
0	0	*[shaded]*
[shaded]	*[shaded]*	3
1		*[shaded]*
[shaded]	*[shaded]*	
2	12	*[shaded]*
[shaded]	*[shaded]*	
3	27	*[shaded]*
[shaded]	*[shaded]*	21
4		*[shaded]*

Helpful hint: change in position = velocity × time interval

EXTENSION The data table that follows is the same kind of table as Data Table 1. Using the information provided in the table, fill in the empty blocks. Do not write in any shaded block. Is the acceleration uniform? Can you find a way to express the dependence of the acceleration on time?

Extension Data Table

Time (seconds)	Position (meters)	Velocity (m/s)
0	0	*[shaded]*
[shaded]	*[shaded]*	1
1		*[shaded]*
[shaded]	*[shaded]*	
2	8	*[shaded]*
[shaded]	*[shaded]*	
3	27	*[shaded]*
[shaded]	*[shaded]*	37
4		*[shaded]*

(continued)

Earth's Gravity and Uniform Acceleration *(continued)*

❓ CONCLUDING QUESTIONS

1. Did your experiment in step 1 turn out the same way Galileo's did? Can you think of some reasons why the experiment might fail? Besides gravity, what other force or forces are acting on the bottles? _____

   _____

   _____

2. Did your experiment in step 2 turn out the same way Galileo's did? In what way is this a slightly less fair test of the constant acceleration caused by Earth's gravity? _____

   _____

   _____

3. Step 3 is a *really* unfair test of Galileo's results. Why? How might you improve the experiment to eliminate this unfairness? (**Hint:** During one of the *Apollo* missions to the moon in the early 1970's, one of the astronauts was filmed dropping a hammer and a feather to the lunar surface at the same time. They landed simultaneously. Would the same result be observed on Earth?)

   _____

   _____

   _____

4. The acceleration of gravity at the surface of another planet would probably have a different value than on Earth, but in all other respects, gravity and its effects would behave in the same way. Examine the completed Data Table 1. What is the value of **g** for this imaginary planet?

   _____

🦅 Follow-up Activities 🦅

1. Imagine the absurd situations that could occur if Galileo were wrong and if heavier objects did fall faster than light ones. For example, consider the idea of using a rock for a parachute. Imagine that someone plans to jump from a tall building. He wants to land safely so, as he jumps, he holds onto a small rock, reasoning that since the rock will fall more slowly than he will, it will act as a parachute! Think of another such absurd situation.

2. Galileo was one of the greatest scientists ever. Research and write a report on his life and his contributions to physics.

Ballistics

 INSTRUCTIONAL OBJECTIVES

Students will be able to

- demonstrate that near Earth's surface, vertical motion under the influence of gravity is independent of horizontal motion.
- understand that the horizontal motion of an object in free flight is at constant speed, ignoring air resistance.

 NATIONAL SCIENCE STANDARDS ADDRESSED

Students demonstrate an understanding of

- motions and forces, gravity.

Students demonstrate scientific inquiry and problem-solving skills by

- framing questions.
- identifying variables in an experimental setting.
- using relevant concepts to explain observations.

Students demonstrate effective scientific communication by

- arguing from evidence.

 **MATERIALS**

- Two coins (quarters)
- A small, flat stick, such as a tongue depressor or ice cream pop stick, or a piece of thin, stiff cardboard cut about 10 to 15 cm long and 1 cm wide
- Wooden or stiff plastic ruler
- Hardcover book
- Table, desk, counter, or bench

HELPFUL HINTS AND DISCUSSION

Time frame: 30 minutes, or a single period of instruction

Structure: Groups of two or three students

Location: In class

Placing the coins on the stick so that the first will easily be dislodged while the second will simply fall may take some practice. Encourage the students to be patient, and try it many times to make sure they can do it. The Follow-up Activity is not meant to encourage violent play, but the games suggested are good, accessible simulations of the physical phenomenon being investigated.

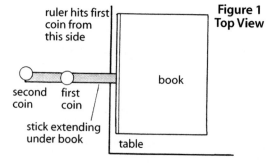

Figure 1 Top View

ruler hits first coin from this side

second coin

first coin

stick extending under book

book

table

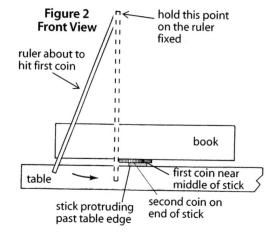

Figure 2 Front View

hold this point on the ruler fixed

ruler about to hit first coin

table

stick protruding past table edge

book

first coin near middle of stick

second coin on end of stick

ADAPTATIONS FOR HIGH AND LOW ACHIEVERS

High Achievers: Encourage these students to do the Follow-Up Activity.

Low Achievers: These students might benefit from grouping with high achievers.

SCORING RUBRIC

Full credit can be given to students who conclude that both coins hit the floor at the same time and who answer the questions correctly and in complete sentences. The quiz can be scored from 1 to 5 correct: one point each for questions 1–3, and one-half point for each of four parts of question 4.

 **INTERNET TIE-INS**   http://www.wsu.edu:8080/~galileo/201projf95/Kreiger/
http://theory.uwinnipeg.ca/physics/twodim/node9.html

 QUIZ
1. Why is motion of an object in free flight usually separated into horizontal and vertical components?
2. True or false: The faster you throw a ball *horizontally*, the longer it will take to hit the floor.
3. What is the effect of air resistance on an object in free flight?
4. Which of the following are examples of ballistics, and which are not?
   (a) a space shuttle lifting off from a launch pad
   (b) an egg falling after it rolls off a table
   (c) a leaf fluttering to the ground
   (d) a basketball arcing upward toward the hoop

Name _____   Date _____

Ballistics

  BEFORE YOU BEGIN

Any object that is dropped, thrown, or shot is called a **projectile**. The study of projectile motion is called **ballistics**. Examples include a batted baseball arcing to the outfield, an egg dropping to the floor, and a shell fired from a cannon. In all these cases, once the object is released, the only significant force acting on it is gravity. Under these conditions an object is said to be in **free flight**.

The motion of a projectile is usually separated into horizontal and vertical components, like the *x*- and *y*-axes of the Cartesian coordinate system that we use to describe vectors. Near the Earth's surface, gravity acts only downward, perpendicular to the surface of the Earth. It therefore has **no effect** on the *horizontal* motion of an object parallel to the surface of the Earth. In free flight there are no forces acting horizontally, so the projectile moves with constant horizontal velocity. This fact agrees with Newton's First Law, which states that an object will maintain a constant velocity unless acted upon by an outside force. This velocity is whatever horizontal velocity the object starts with when it begins its free flight. If we view the object from above so that the vertical motion is not seen, the object does not appear to speed up or slow down during the flight.

In some cases the slowing effect of **air resistance**, a form of friction, must be considered. If air resistance is significant, as in tossing a paper airplane or a Frisbee™, the problem is no longer one of ballistics, but of **aerodynamics**. Under ordinary Earthbound conditions, free flight does not last very long. Eventually, the object collides with something or is subjected to other forces, and the free flight is over.

 MATERIALS

- Two coins (quarters)
- A small, flat stick, such as a tongue depressor or ice cream pop stick, or a piece of thin, stiff cardboard cut about 10 to 15 cm long and 1 cm wide

- Wooden or stiff plastic ruler
- Hardcover book
- Table, desk, counter, or bench

 PROCEDURE

1. Hold the stick flat on the table with about two thirds of its length hanging past the edge of the table. Place the book on top of the other one third of the stick to hold it in place.

2. Place one coin flat on the stick about midway between the tip of the stick and the edge of the table, extending a bit past both sides of the stick. Place a second coin on the tip of the stick, barely balanced and ready to fall off. See Figure 1.

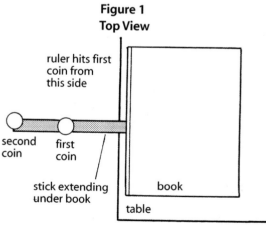

Figure 1
Top View

ruler hits first coin from this side

second coin

first coin

stick extending under book

book

table

© 1999 J. Weston Walch, Publisher

54

Walch Hands-on Science Series: Force and Motion

(continued)

Ballistics *(continued)*

3. Hold the ruler in a hanging position above the stick. Hold it by its top end so that it can swing. Position the ruler so that when you swing it, it will hit the first coin squarely and propel it forward. See Figure 2.

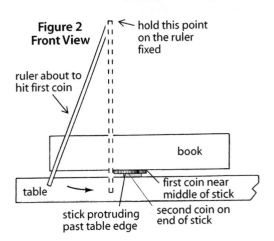

**Figure 2
Front View**

hold this point
on the ruler
fixed

ruler about to
hit first coin

book

table

stick protruding
past table edge

first coin near
middle of stick

second coin on
end of stick

Be sure there are unobstructed paths for the coins to reach the floor without hitting anything. Swing or pull the bottom of the ruler away from the stick, and then swing it sharply forward to strike the first coin to propel it in the *horizontal* direction. Try to avoid giving the coin any velocity upward or downward. This may take some practice. The second coin should drop straight down to the floor. Observe and record which coin hits the floor first, or if it is a tie.

4. Repeat step 3 twice more for a total of three trials. Try varying the force with which you strike the first coin.

DATA COLLECTION AND ANALYSIS

Check which coin strikes the floor first (three trials):

First coin _____ Second coin _____ Tie _____

First coin _____ Second coin _____ Tie _____

First coin _____ Second coin _____ Tie _____

CONCLUDING QUESTIONS

1. Which coin (the one struck by the ruler or the one dropping straight down) hits the floor first?

Why? _____

_____

2. Think of the second coin (the one that drops straight down) as a timer against which to compare the first coin's flight time until it hits the floor. Does the time it takes for the first coin to hit the floor depend on how far it flies across the room? Why or why not?

_____

_____

(continued)

Ballistics *(continued)*

⤷ Follow-up Activity ⤶

It is unfortunate but true that some scientific discoveries are used in war. Even Galileo's ballistics studies were prompted by the need to improve the accuracy of weapons. There are many arcade-style games with names like "Artillery" or "Armor" for Windows and Macintosh personal computers that simulate tanks or artillery firing at targets. Many of these are freeware or shareware and can be obtained over the Internet from such sites as *shareware.com* and *filemine.com*. Despite their violent themes, some of these games can give you a good appreciation for the physics of projectiles.

The Pendulum

 INSTRUCTIONAL OBJECTIVES

Students will be able to

- understand the concept of periodic motion.
- demonstrate the relationship between the length and period of a pendulum.

 NATIONAL SCIENCE STANDARDS ADDRESSED

Students demonstrate an understanding of

- motions and forces, gravity.

Students demonstrate scientific inquiry and problem-solving skills by

- using concepts to explain phenomena.
- identifying and controlling variables in experimental and nonexperimental settings.
- working individually and in teams to collect and share information and ideas.

Students demonstrate effective scientific communication by

- arguing from evidence and data.
- representing data in multiple ways.

 MATERIALS

For each pair:

- Strong sewing thread (at least a meter long)
- Ping-pong ball
- Golf ball
- Table, desk, or bench
- Meterstick
- Tape (vinyl electrical tape preferred)
- Triple-beam balance
- Dowel or round pencil
- Heavy object (weight, stack of books, etc.)
- Stopwatch or watch or clock that can display seconds

HELPFUL HINTS AND DISCUSSION

Time frame: 40 minutes, or a single period of instruction
Structure: Pairs of students
Location: In class

Review with students the correct operation of whatever stopwatches or other timing devices they will be using. Have the pairs of students practice coordinating the release of the ball with the start of the stopwatch, as described in step 2. Also review the use of a triple-beam balance.

ADAPTATIONS FOR HIGH AND LOW ACHIEVERS

High Achievers: Encourage these students to do the Extensions and the Follow-Up Activities.

Low Achievers: Review the relevant concepts for these students, especially that a period is a complete cycle—that is, it represents the time for one full back-and-forth motion of the pendulum.

SCORING RUBRIC

Full credit can be given to students who answer the questions correctly and in complete sentences. The quiz can be scored from 1 to 4 correct.

Figure 1

fixed point

rod

weight

Figure 2

  **INTERNET TIE-IN**   http://www.math.rpi.edu/www/diffeq/links/pendulum

QUIZ
1. True or false: The period of a pendulum is the time it takes for the weight to swing from one side to the other.
2. If you shorten the length of a pendulum, what will happen to its period?
3. If you increase the weight at the end of a pendulum, what will happen to its period?
4. Why does a mechanical clock require a wound-up spring?

Name _____ Date _____

The Pendulum

 BEFORE YOU BEGIN

Have you ever seen a grandfather clock? Like any timepiece, it keeps time by causing an event to occur over and over at a constant rate. Nowadays, these events are usually electronic, as in a digital watch or clock, but in a grandfather clock, they are mechanical. The swinging of a **pendulum** back and forth within the clock provides this repetitive motion. A pendulum consists of a weight suspended from a fixed point by a rod (or string, wire, etc.), as shown in Figure 1. The pendulum is just one example of an object that undergoes repetitive motion, also called **periodic** motion. If the weight hangs directly below the fixed point from which it is suspended, it doesn't move. However, if you pull the weight a little to one side and let it go, gravity pulls the weight back toward the straight-down position. The weight swings back down through and beyond the straight-down position because of the velocity it gained while falling. The weight continues swinging up until gravity brings it to a temporary halt again. Then the weight heads back toward the straight-down position again, and the process repeats. The weight swings back and forth. Of course, any real mechanical system has some friction, so without regular pushing the weight will eventually stop at the straight-down position. In a mechanical clock, a wound-up spring provides the necessary push.

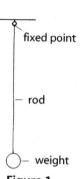

Figure 1

The time the weight takes to move through one full back-and-forth swing (an **oscillation**) is called the **period** of the pendulum. In this activity, you will explore how the length and mass of a pendulum affect its period.

 MATERIALS

For each pair:
- Strong sewing thread (at least a meter long)
- Ping-pong ball
- Golf ball
- Table, desk, or bench
- Meterstick
- Tape (vinyl electrical tape preferred)

- Triple-beam balance
- Dowel or round pencil
- Heavy object (weight, stack of books, etc.)
- Stopwatch or watch or clock that can display seconds

PROCEDURE

1. Place the dowel on the table with about 10 cm of its length hanging over the edge. Hold it in place with the heavy object. Securely tape one end of the sewing thread to the golf ball. Tie the other end of the thread to the dowel so that the center of the ball hangs 75 cm below the center of the dowel. Use the meterstick to set this distance. If the ball begins to spin because the thread has spun around, just wait a few minutes for this spinning to stop.

                   Walch Hands-on Science Series: Force and Motion

(continued)

The Pendulum *(continued)*

Figure 2

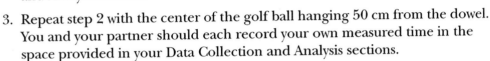

2. Stand nearby with the stopwatch ready. Your partner should pull the golf ball gently to one side, about as shown in Figure 2. At the moment your partner lets go, he or she should say "Now," which is the signal for you to start the stopwatch. Measure the time it takes for the golf ball to swing completely back and forth 10 times. Enter this time in the space provided in **your** Data Collection and Analysis section. Switch tasks with your partner and repeat this step. Your partner should now enter the time in **his/her** Data Collection and Analysis section.

3. Repeat step 2 with the center of the golf ball hanging 50 cm from the dowel. You and your partner should each record your own measured time in the space provided in your Data Collection and Analysis sections.

4. Repeat step 2 with the center of the golf ball hanging 25 cm from the dowel. Again, you and your partner should each record your own measured time in the space provided in your Data Collection and Analysis sections.

5. Replace the golf ball with the ping-pong ball, and repeat step 2 with the ping-pong ball hanging 75 cm from the dowel. You and your partner should each record your own measured time in the space provided in your Data Collection and Analysis sections. You will notice that the ping-pong ball swings a shorter distance on each successive swing, but this should not affect your timing results.

6. Using the triple-beam balance, measure the weight of the golf ball and then the ping-pong ball in grams. Record these measurements in the space provided in your Data Collection and Analysis sections.

7. For each of the three lengths of string, find the period of the pendulum by dividing the time you measured by 10. Enter your results in the boxed charts in the Data Collection and Analysis section. Divide the weight of the golf ball by the weight of the ping-pong ball and enter this **ratio** in the space provided.

 EXTENSION

Graph your data from steps 2 through 4, with string length on the horizontal axis and period calculated in step 7 on the vertical axis. Make the range of the horizontal axis 0 to 100 cm, and the range of the vertical axis 0 to 3 seconds.

(continued)

Name _____   Date _____

The Pendulum (continued)

 DATA COLLECTION AND ANALYSIS

Partner #1

Golf ball

75 cm   time for 10 oscillations _____ seconds, period _____ seconds

50 cm   time for 10 oscillations _____ seconds, period _____ seconds

25 cm   time for 10 oscillations _____ seconds, period _____ seconds

Ping-pong ball

75 cm   time for 10 oscillations _____ seconds, period _____ seconds

Partner #2

Golf ball

75 cm   time for 10 oscillations _____ seconds, period _____ seconds

50 cm   time for 10 oscillations _____ seconds, period _____ seconds

25 cm   time for 10 oscillations _____ seconds, period _____ seconds

Ping-pong ball

75 cm   time for 10 oscillations _____ seconds, period _____ seconds

Weight of golf ball: _____ g

Weight of ping-pong ball: _____ g

Ratio ($\frac{\text{weight of golf ball}}{\text{weight of ping-pong ball}}$): _____

CONCLUDING QUESTIONS

1. In steps 2 through 4, what happened to the period of the pendulum as the string got shorter?

    _____

    _____

    _____

(continued)

The Pendulum (continued)

2. If you increased the length of the string to 1 meter, would you predict the period of the pendulum to be greater or less than the period at 75 cm? Why? _____

_____

_____

_____

3. How many times heavier (more massive) is the golf ball than the ping-pong ball? With the length of the string at 75 cm, did the the period of the pendulum change significantly when you replaced the golf ball with the ping-pong ball? Does the period of a pendulum depend on how heavy the weight is? _____

_____

_____

_____

 EXTENSION

If the period of a pendulum were directly proportional to the length of the string, the period would change just about as much going from 75 cm to 50 cm as it did going from 50 cm to 25 cm. Did this happen? Can you think of another possible relationship between length and period that would work? _____

_____

_____

_____

🌀 Follow-up Activities 🌀

There are many examples of periodic motion in ordinary life. Make a list of at least five objects in which something returns to a paricular position with a regular period.

 EXTENSION

Research the behavior of simple pendulums, and write a brief report.

Orbital Motion

 Instructional Objectives

Students will be able to

- understand what it means for an object to be in orbit.
- describe the relationship between orbital radius and orbital period.

 National Science Standards Addressed

Students demonstrate an understanding of

- motions and forces.

Students demonstrate scientific inquiry and problem-solving skills by

- using concepts to explain phenomena.
- identifying and controlling variables in experimental and nonexperimental settings.
- working individually and in teams to collect and share information and ideas.

Students demonstrate effective scientific communication by

- arguing from evidence and data.
- representing data in multiple ways.

 Materials

- Modeling clay about the size of a golf ball
- String
- Scissors
- Meterstick
- Pen or pencil
- Sheet of graph paper, $8\frac{1}{2}'' \times 11''$
- Watch or clock with a second hand or readout

Helpful Hints and Discussion

Time frame:	40 minutes, or a single period of instruction
Structure:	Part A: Pairs; Part B: Individuals
Location:	In class

Instruct the students to embed the end of the string solidly in the center of the clay ball. Also make sure they don't swing the clay ball around either too vigorously or over their heads; it should be swung gently while hanging downward.

Adaptations for High and Low Achievers

High Achievers: Encourage these students to do the Extension and the Follow-Up Activities.

Low Achievers: Review the relevant concepts for these students. In particular, review graphing and choosing appropriate scales for the two axes. Low achievers can be paired with high achievers for Part A.

Figure 1

Figure 2

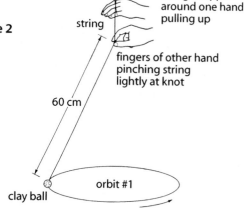

Figure 3

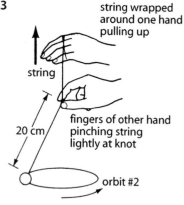

62

SCORING RUBRIC

Full credit can be given to students who give reasonable answers to the questions in complete sentences. The quiz can be scored from 1 to 4 correct.

 **INTERNET TIE-INS**   http://liftoff.msfc.nasa.gov/academy/rocket_sci/orbmech/VEL_CALC.HTML
http://webphysics.iupui.edu/gpnew/gp2sup1.htm (includes Kepler's Laws of Planetary Motion and Newton's Laws)

 QUIZ
1. True or false: An object in orbit around the earth is no longer acted on by gravity.
2. If the earth were flat, would it be possible for an object to be in orbit? Why or why not?
3. What is meant by the period of an object in orbit?
4. How does the period of an object in orbit depend on the radius of the orbit?

Orbital Motion

  BEFORE YOU BEGIN

If you drop a ball, it falls straight down because of Earth's gravity. If you throw a ball horizontally, it still falls, but it travels some distance before hitting the ground. If you throw it faster, it travels even farther before hitting the ground. Now imagine throwing the ball so fast that it travels far enough for the curved surface of the earth to drop away under it as it falls. See Figure 1. Gravity still acts on it and the ball is still constantly falling toward the earth, but because the earth is round, the ball never strikes the ground. The ball is now **in orbit** around the earth. An object in orbit around a larger object is called a **satellite**, whether natural or artificial. The horizontal speed required for an object to be in a low circular orbit about 150 km above the surface of the earth is about 7 km/sec or 28,400 km/hr, about 180 times faster than a major league fastball!

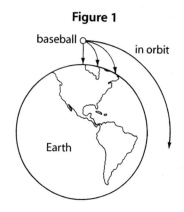

Figure 1

The time it takes for an object to complete one orbit is called a **period**. The larger the radius of the orbit, the longer the orbital period. There are two reasons for this: A larger orbit has a larger circumference for the object to cover, and the speed of an object in a larger orbit is slower. These two facts combine to make the period of the orbit increase as you go from a smaller orbit to a larger one.

Real orbits have many shapes, but circles are easiest to work with. Therefore, in this exercise you will examine circular orbits. Since you can't create a real gravitational orbit in your classroom or at home, you will use a clay ball to simulate a satellite and a string to simulate gravity.

 ## MATERIALS

- Modeling clay about the size of a golf ball
- String
- Scissors
- Meterstick
- Pen or pencil
- Sheet of graph paper, $8\frac{1}{2}" \times 11"$
- Watch or clock with a second hand or readout

 ## PROCEDURE

PART A

> **Note: You and your partner should each do steps 1 through 4 independently.**

1. Cut a piece of string about 80 cm long. Take one end of the string and mold the ball of clay around it to hold it securely.

2. Tie knots in the string 20 cm and 60 cm from the clay ball.

3. Wrap the end of the string around the fingers of one hand a few times up to the 60-cm knot so that the length of string from the 60-cm knot to the clay ball is free.

(continued)

Orbital Motion *(continued)*

4. With the thumb and forefinger of your other hand, lightly pinch the hanging string at a point just under the 60-cm knot. See Figure 2. This should not affect the motion of the ball. Start the ball of clay moving in a circle by **slowly** moving your hands in a circle, keeping your hands close together. Once the ball is moving smoothly in a circle, stop moving your hand. The ball should keep circling. It may take a few tries to get the ball moving smoothly.

Note: Read steps 5 and 6 and then do some practice runs before proceeding. You and your partner should take turns being "string holder" or "timer" for steps 5 and 6. Practice these steps as many times as needed to achieve a smooth pull on the string and a good count for each of the 10-second intervals. Do not record any of the results for these practice runs. When you are both ready, proceed, starting with step 5.

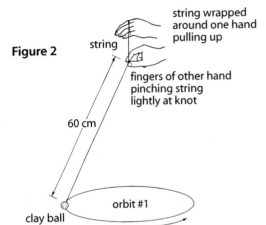

Figure 2

string wrapped around one hand pulling up

string

fingers of other hand pinching string lightly at knot

60 cm

orbit #1

clay ball

5. Once the string holder has the ball moving smoothly, the timer should start timing Orbit #1, calling out "Go!" The timer should then call out when 10 seconds have passed, and again when another 10 seconds have passed. During the first 10 seconds, the string holder should count the number of complete circles (orbits) made by the ball. Record this number in the Data Collection and Analysis section.

6. As soon as the timer calls out the first 10 seconds, the string holder smoothly and quickly pulls straight up with the hand with the wrapped string, shortening the swinging string to the 20-cm knot. See Figure 3. During the second 10 seconds, the string holder again counts the number of circles made by the ball in Orbit #2. Again, record this number in the Data Collection and Analysis section.

7. Repeat steps 5 and 6 (including data recording), switching timer and string holder tasks.

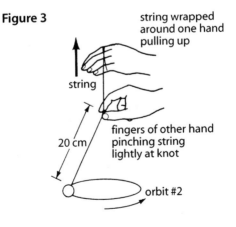

Figure 3

string wrapped around one hand pulling up

string

fingers of other hand pinching string lightly at knot

20 cm

orbit #2

(continued)

Orbital Motion *(continued)*

PART B

1. The data table below lists values for the orbital radius (radius of an orbit measured from the center of the earth), orbital altitude (altitude of the orbit above Earth's surface), and orbital period (time to complete one orbit) for some possible circular orbits around the earth. The radius of the earth is approximately 6,400 km. On the graph paper, make a graph of the altitude versus the period. Plot altitude on the *x*-axis (horizontal) and period on the *y*-axis (vertical). Connect the points smoothly with straight lines.

Orbital Radius (km)	Orbital Altitude (km)	Orbital Period (hr)
6,600	200	1.5
7,400	1,000	1.8
12,900	6,500	4
16,400	10,000	6
26,378	20,000	12
42,200	35,800	24

DATA COLLECTION AND ANALYSIS

PART A

First string holder:

   Number of orbits in 10 seconds (string long) _____

   Number of orbits in 10 seconds (string short) _____

Second string holder:

   Number of orbits in 10 seconds (string long) _____

   Number of orbits in 10 seconds (string short) _____

PART B

EXTENSION Find out the orbital altitude for the Hubble Space Telescope. Replot the graph with an appropriate range of altitudes in order to better determine Hubble's orbital period from your graph.

CONCLUDING QUESTIONS

PART A

1. What do you conclude happens to the period of the ball's orbit as the string gets shorter?

_____

_____

_____

_____

(continued)

Walch Hands-on Science Series: Force and Motion

Orbital Motion *(continued)*

2. How do your results for the number of orbits compare with your partner's in both the long-string and short-string steps? What are some possible reasons for any discrepancies?

_____

_____

_____

_____

PART B

1. At about what orbital altitude would an object have an orbital period of 15 hours?

_____

2. Describe what happens to the orbital period as the orbital radius increases. _____

_____

_____

3. What do you notice about the orbital period for an orbital radius of 42,200 km? For a satellite in such an orbit around the earth's equator, how will its position in the sky change from hour to hour or from day to day? Relate this conclusion to satellite communications. _____

_____

_____

_____

_____

_____

EXTENSION What is the orbital period of the Hubble Space Telescope?

⪼ Follow-up Activities ⪼

1. As mentioned in the "Before You Begin" section, real orbits are usually not circular. Research the shapes of orbits, and write a brief report. Include both closed, repeating orbits and open, nonrepeating ones.
2. Visit the website at http://www.osf.hq.nasa.gov/mir/mirvis.html to find out if, when, and in what direction the Russian space station Mir is visible from your location. If so, try to see it.
3. Visit the website at http://liftoff.msfc.nasa.gov/RealTime/JTrack/Spacecraft.html for a real-time map of astronomical satellite positions (requires Java).

Momentum

 INSTRUCTIONAL OBJECTIVES

Students will be able to
- describe the concept of momentum.
- demonstrate transfer of momentum.

 NATIONAL SCIENCE STANDARDS ADDRESSED

Students demonstrate an understanding of
- properties of matter.
- motions and forces.
- momentum.
- relevant concepts to explain observed phenomena.

Students demonstrate scientific inquiry and problem-solving skills by
- framing questions.
- identifying and controlling variables in experimental settings.
- working in teams to collect and share information and ideas.

Students demonstrate effective scientific communication by
- arguing from evidence and data.

 MATERIALS
- Regular (wood or aluminum) baseball bat
- Plastic toy baseball bat
- Hard plastic toy baseball (**not** a regular baseball and **not** a Wiffle™ ball)
- A baseball field or other open space
- 10 sheets of paper
- 10 small rocks
- Laboratory scale that can weigh up to 2 kg

 INTERNET TIE-INS   http://tqd.advanced.org/3042/linear.html
http://www.math-science.sfasu.edu/physics101/Momentum.html

HELPFUL HINTS AND DISCUSSION

Time frame: 40–50 minutes
Structure: Groups of two to four students
Location: At an appropriate open space outside of class time; analysis and concluding questions in class

Each group of students may determine its own time to use a baseball field or other open space. You may want to organize groups of students after determining who has access to the various materials used in the activity. Otherwise, you may decide to stock a small supply of plastic toy bats and balls to lend to some groups. Make sure that the retrievers remain aware of the batter's actions while they are out in the field. The students will do the baseball part of the activity outside of school hours and then do the remainder in class.

ADAPTATIONS FOR HIGH AND LOW ACHIEVERS

There should be no need to distinguish between high and low achievers for this activity. High achievers should be encouraged to do the Extension and the Follow-Up Activity.

SCORING RUBRIC

Full credit can be given to students who calculate their averages correctly and who answer the questions correctly and in complete sentences. The quiz can be scored from 1 to 4 correct.

 **QUIZ**
1. Define *momentum* in words. Then define it with a mathematical expression, including units.
2. What will happen to the momentum of a locomotive if its speed is doubled?
3. Write the following down in order of increasing momentum:
   (a) a bird flying at 20 miles per hour
   (b) an airplane traveling at 200 miles per hour
   (c) a snail crawling at 0.0002 miles per hour
   (d) a race car traveling at 200 miles per hour
4. True or false: Momentum cannot be transferred from one object to another

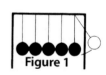

Figure 1

Figure 2

Momentum

 BEFORE YOU BEGIN

Imagine playing catch with a friend. If the ball is tossed to you gently, it's easy to stop it with your hand. If the same ball is thrown much harder to you, it will be much harder to stop. Newton's First Law of Motion tells you that an object in motion tends to stay in motion, and so the ball does. Because of this, your hand may even move back a bit when the ball hits it. In this exercise, you will explore the physical quantity called **momentum**, which measures the tendency of a moving body to remain in motion.

We know from experience that stopping an object that is moving fast is more difficult than stopping a similar one that is moving slowly. We also know that it is harder to stop a more massive object than a lighter one when both are moving at the same velocity. Combining these observations, we want a quantity that is a combination of mass and velocity, so we define the momentum of an object as the *product* of its mass and its velocity. Because velocity is a vector quantity, momentum is also. Its direction is the same as the direction of its velocity. Momentum has units of kilograms times meters per second (kg•m/s). For example, the momentum of an average car traveling at 55 miles per hour is about 35,000 kg•m/s, while the momentum of a flitting butterfly is about 0.001 kg•m/s.

One of the most important properties of momentum is that it can be transferred from one object to another. Imagine a friend standing still on ice skates. Your friend has zero momentum. Now imagine pitching a baseball to your friend, who catches it. If the pitch is fast enough, your friend will slide backward. The momentum that the baseball had is now shared with your friend.

 MATERIALS

- Regular (wood or aluminum) baseball bat
- Plastic toy baseball bat
- Hard plastic toy baseball (**not** a regular baseball and **not** a Wiffle™ ball)

- A baseball field or other open space
- 10 sheets of paper
- 10 small rocks
- Laboratory scale that can weigh up to 2 kg

 PROCEDURE

Steps 1 through 5 should be done by each member of your group, with assistance from the other members.

1. Stand at home plate or in a corner of the field. ⑊ (**Safety note: Make sure you are far enough away from buildings or other people. The student retrieving balls should be careful to watch the batter at all times.**) Using the regular baseball bat and the toy baseball, hit a fly ball as far as you can. Your partners should mark the place where the ball lands with a piece of paper using a rock to hold the paper in place. Be sure to mark the position where the ball *first* hits the ground, not where it bounces or rolls to. It's okay to keep trying until you hit the ball solidly. Your partners should return the ball after marking the landing spot.

2. Repeat the first step 9 more times, for a total of 10 trials.

3. Find the three farthest hits. Pace off the distance to each of these spots from the place where the batter was standing, and record these distances in the Data Collection and Analysis section.

(continued)

Momentum *(continued)*

4. Repeat steps 1 through 3 using the plastic toy baseball bat. Again, try to hit the ball as far as you can, and record your farthest three hits.

5. Weigh both of the bats using the scale, and record their masses in the space provided.

DATA COLLECTION AND ANALYSIS

- **Distances (in paces) ball is hit with regular baseball bat:**

   Farthest   _____

   Second farthest   _____

   Third farthest   _____

   Calculate and enter the average of these three distances: _____

   Mass of regular bat   _____ grams

- **Distances (in paces) ball is hit with plastic baseball bat:**

   Farthest   _____

   Second farthest   _____

   Third farthest   _____

   Calculate and enter the average of these three distances: _____

   Mass of plastic bat   _____ grams

CONCLUDING QUESTIONS

1. Batting a ball involves transferring momentum from what object to what other object? Is all of the first object's momentum transferred? _____

   _____

2. For which bat did you obtain the farther average distance? What does this say about the relative amount of momentum given to the ball by the two bats? _____

   _____

3. Assuming that all bats give the same fraction of their momentum to the ball, which bat had the greater momentum? _____

   _____

4. Assume that if you swing as hard as you can, the velocity of the bat is about the same for both bats. What relative property of the two bats accounts for your answer to the previous question? Does this agree with your measurement in step 5? _____

   _____

(continued)

Momentum *(continued)*

 EXTENSION

Ask the other members of your group for their data from this activity. Describe any differences in the average distances calculated for the members of your group. What factors may be responsible for these differences? _____

_____

_____

 Follow-up Activity

A popular desk toy you have probably seen is a frame on which a row of several identical metal spheres is suspended on strings. If you pull one sphere away from the others, as in Figure 1, and let it go so it hits the row of remaining spheres, the sphere on the other end of the row swings away from the others, as in Figure 2. When it swings back and hits the row, the process repeats in reverse, and so on, back and forth. Based on what you have learned in this activity, explain how this device works.

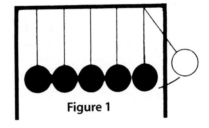

Figure 1

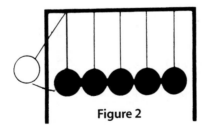

Figure 2

Work (the Physics Kind)

✓ INSTRUCTIONAL OBJECTIVES

Students will be able to

- describe the physical concept of work.
- demonstrate work.

🌐 NATIONAL SCIENCE STANDARDS ADDRESSED

Students demonstrate an understanding of

- properties of matter.
- motions and forces.
- relevant concepts to explain observed phenomena.

Students demonstrate scientific inquiry and problem-solving skills by

- framing questions.
- identifying and controlling variables in experimental settings.
- working in teams to collect and share information and ideas.

Students demonstrate effective scientific communication by

- arguing from evidence and data.

✂ MATERIALS

For each pair:

- Spring scale (range 4 to10 pounds preferred)
- Smooth floor
- A supply of books, either hardcover or softcover
- Cardboard box large enough to fit about 10 books
- Meterstick or tape measure
- Masking tape

SCORING RUBRIC

Full credit can be given to students who calculate the values of work correctly and who answer the questions correctly and in complete sentences. The quiz can be scored from 1 to 4 correct.

HELPFUL HINTS AND DISCUSSION

Time frame: 40–50 minutes
Structure: Pairs of students
Location: In class

Try this exercise with materials on hand before giving them to the students. If no floor or table works well, try using a sheet of plywood or paneling to provide a more uniform surface. Remind the students to pull horizontally in step 2, making sure that they do not cause the front edge of the box to rise as they pull. Encourage them to practice pulling on the scale with uniform force before they proceed to step 3. When a student pulls the box with the spring scale, the reading on the scale may briefly go high until the box breaks free of the static friction; then it will settle down to a constant reading as the student pulls slowly and uniformly. Students should ignore the initial high force reading and record the force during steady motion. This activity should ordinarily be assigned after "Friction." Students in a group may collect common data, but each should do his or her own calculations and Concluding Questions.

ADAPTATIONS FOR HIGH AND LOW ACHIEVERS

High Achievers: Encourage these students to do the Extensions and the Follow-Up Activity. They can also be guided to texts with a more mathematical treatment of the subject.

Low Achievers: Review the relevant concepts, such as force, weight, and friction, for these students. They can be paired with high achievers for the exercise.

💻 INTERNET TIE-IN http://www.glenbrook.k12.il.us/gbssci/phys/Class/energy/energytoc.html

❓ QUIZ
1. Define work in the physics sense.
2. What will happen to the work done if the magnitude of the applied force is doubled?
3. What will happen to the work done if the distance over which the force is applied is cut in half?
4. True or false: No work is done on your schoolbooks when you pick them up from the floor.

Name _____   Date _____

Work (the Physics Kind)

 BEFORE YOU BEGIN

When you hear the word *work*, a wide range of activities may come to mind. You may imagine taking out the trash, studying for a history exam, or mowing the lawn. In physics, however, "work" has a very specific meaning. Think about pulling a bowl of pasta across the dinner table toward you. You exert a force on the bowl to counteract the force of friction that resists the bowl's sliding. As a result, the bowl moves a certain distance. **Work** (W) is defined as the magnitude of the force (F) exerted on an object, multiplied by the distance (d) traveled by the object *in the same direction as the force* while the force is acting.

$$W = F \times d$$

The amount of work done will increase if the magnitude of the force is increased, if the force acts on the object over a greater distance, or both. Notice that work is a scalar quantity, even though force is a vector.

Work can be either positive or negative. If you push a car on level ground and it rolls away from you, the force you exert does positive work on it. If the car is rolling downhill toward you and you try to hold it back, you might exert exactly the same force on the car. However, since the direction of motion is opposite the direction of the force, the work done by you on the car is negative. In this case, the car does work on you! Work is done only if something is moved to a different location than its starting point. You might push with all your might against a building and quickly become exhausted, but unless the building moves, no work has been done on it!

 MATERIALS

For each pair:
- Spring scale (range 4 to10 pounds preferred)
- Smooth floor
- A supply of books, either hardcover or softcover
- Cardboard box large enough to fit about 10 books
- Meterstick or tape measure
- Masking tape

 PROCEDURE

1. Place the cardboard box on the floor. Put three to five books into the box, and hook the spring scale to the box. You may need to punch a hole in the box to attach the end of the hook.

2. Holding onto the other end of the spring scale, drag the box in a straight line *slowly* across the floor. Make sure that the scale reads a constant force (weight) in the low half of the scale's range. Reduce the number of books in the box if the scale reads too high. Add books if the scale measures little or no force. Pull *horizontally*. Do not allow the spring scale to lift the box. Read the force on the scale only while the box is moving at constant speed, not when starting up or coming to a stop. Practice until you feel comfortable doing this.

3. Place a small piece of masking tape on the floor at the front edge of the box to indicate the box's starting position. Drag the box a short distance (less than a meter) in a straight line, moving the box slowly and keeping a constant force. Record the force in the Data Collection and Analysis section. Then, measure the distance traveled by the box, and record this value.

(continued)

Work (the Physics Kind) *(continued)*

4. Repeat step 3, but this time move the box several times as far as you did in step 3. Try to use the same force as you did in step 3. Again, measure and record the force and the distance the box traveled in the Data Collection and Analysis section.

5. Add three to five books to the cardboard box. Repeat step 3 again, and move the box the same distance you moved it in step 3. Measure and record the force you exerted and the distance the box traveled in the Data Collection and Analysis section.

EXTENSION

Repeat step 4, this time moving the box the same distance but about twice as fast as you did in step 4. Measure and record the force and the distance the box traveled in the space provided.

DATA COLLECTION AND ANALYSIS

If your scale reads in pounds, convert to newtons (1 pound = 4.45 N).
If your tape measure reads in inches, convert to meters (1 m = 39.4 inches).
In each line below, use your measured values for force and distance to calculate the work you did in dragging the box.

Step 3:	force = _____ N	distance = _____ meters	work = _____ N-m
Step 4:	force = _____ N	distance = _____ meters	work = _____ N-m
Step 5:	force = _____ N	distance = _____ meters	work = _____ N-m

EXTENSION

Step 6	force = _____ N	distance = _____ meters	work = _____ N-m

CONCLUDING QUESTIONS

1. Does the work done increase or decrease when you increase the distance you drag the cardboard box? _____

2. Why does adding books to the box change the result in step 5? _____
_____

3. Does the work done increase or decrease when the force required to drag the cardboard box is increased? _____

EXTENSION

In step 6 you moved the box at about twice the speed you used in step 4. Did the work done by you on the box also double? Does work in the physics sense depend significantly on how fast the object is moved? _____
_____
_____

(continued)

Work (the Physics Kind) *(continued)*

Follow-up Activity

Borrow a spring scale and bring it home. Make a list of at least five ordinary tasks that you think involve work of the physics kind (like putting a stack of clean dishes away in the cabinet). Using either the spring scale or a bathroom scale, and a tape measure or ruler to measure distance, estimate the work done in newton-meters to do that task. Once this is done, put your list of tasks in order from the greatest to least amount of work. (**Hints:** Keep the tasks **simple** and **safe**. Carrying an *unopened* gallon of paint up a flight of stairs is okay, but rebuilding an automobile transmission is not. Also, note that if you slowly lift an object, the upward force you exert on it is approximately equal to its weight.)

Kinetic Energy

 INSTRUCTIONAL OBJECTIVES

Students will be able to

- describe the concept of kinetic energy.
- demonstrate work done by kinetic energy.

 NATIONAL SCIENCE STANDARDS ADDRESSED

Students demonstrate an understanding of

- properties of matter.
- motions and forces.
- relevant concepts to explain observed phenomena.

Students demonstrate scientific inquiry and problem-solving skills by

- framing questions.
- identifying and controlling variables in experimental settings.
- working in teams to collect and share information and ideas.

Students demonstrate effective scientific communication by

- arguing from evidence and data.

 MATERIALS

- A crushable foam block
- Golf ball
- Calculator
- Ladder or stepstool
- Tape measure (preferably metric)
- Ruler marked in centimeters and millimeters
- Felt-tip marker
- One sheet of graph paper for each student
- Pen or pencil
- Balance (extension activity)

HELPFUL HINTS AND DISCUSSION

Time frame: 40–50 minutes
Structure: Groups of two to four students
Location: In class

The crushable foam needed for this activity is the kind florists use to support the stems of flowers in dried flower arrangements. It may go by the name "Sahara" and can be obtained from florists and some hardware and crafts stores. The correct type of foam dents easily and retains any indentation without springing back. Each group of students should need only one block, since they can use the four largest faces for the activity. Each student should use no more than one flat surface of the foam block. Encourage all students to practice dropping the golf ball on a target before using the foam block.

Be sure that all students use the ladder safely.

ADAPTATIONS FOR HIGH AND LOW ACHIEVERS

High Achievers: Encourage these students to do the Extensions and the Follow-Up Activity.

Low Achievers: Review the relevant concepts of mass and velocity for these students. Make sure that they know how to use a calculator to calculate a fourth power.

SCORING RUBRIC

Full credit can be given to students who complete the experiment and who answer the questions correctly and in complete sentences. The quiz can be scored from 1 to 4 correct.

 INTERNET TIE-IN   http://www.glenbrook.k12.il.us/gbssci/phys/Class/energy/u5l1c.html

 **QUIZ**
1. What is the mathematical formula for kinetic energy?
2. How much kinetic energy does an object have if it is at rest?
3. What will happen to an object's kinetic energy if its velocity is doubled?
4. True or false: Kinetic energy can be either positive or negative.

Kinetic Energy

✎ BEFORE YOU BEGIN

Have you ever been hit accidentally by a stray volleyball, basketball, tennis ball, or baseball? If the ball was moving slowly, you might not have felt much, but if it was moving at a high speed, then you undoubtedly felt something unpleasant. The difference between the effects in these two cases has to do with energy.

Objects can possess energy in many forms. A moving object possesses energy because of its motion. This is called **kinetic energy**. Like momentum, kinetic energy (KE) depends on both the mass and the velocity of the object. Unlike momentum, however, kinetic energy depends on the *square* of the velocity:

$$KE = \tfrac{1}{2}\,mv^2$$

Momentum is related to an object's tendency to stay in motion, while kinetic energy is related to how much work the object can do because of its motion. Like potential energy, kinetic energy is a scalar quantity.

Different kinds of energy can be converted into each other. As we've discussed in an earlier activity, when you raise an object off the ground and hold it up, you increase its potential energy. However, it has no kinetic energy. If you then drop the object, the potential energy is converted to kinetic energy, which is greatest just before the object hits the ground. As it hits, some or all of the kinetic energy gets converted to other forms of energy, such as heat and sound.

Kinetic energy is difficult to measure directly using an instrument. Instead, we usually measure mass and velocity and calculate the kinetic energy. Otherwise, we can measure some effect that the object creates when it gives up its kinetic energy. In this exercise the size of a dent made in a foam block will be used as a rough indicator of the kinetic energy transferred from a dropped object to the foam.

 MATERIALS

- A crushable foam block
- Golf ball
- Calculator
- Ladder or stepstool
- Tape measure (preferably metric)

- Ruler marked in centimeters and millimeters
- Felt-tip marker
- One sheet of graph paper for each student
- Pen or pencil
- Balance (extension activity)

 PROCEDURE

Each member of your group should carry out the entire procedure with the assistance of other members of the group as indicated.

1. Place the block of foam on the floor or ground.
2. Hold the golf ball *directly above* the block of foam at a height of $\tfrac{1}{2}$ meter (20 inches) from the top surface of the foam. To measure the correct height, have a member of your group hold the tape measure vertically, with the 0 mark at the top surface of the foam. Drop the golf ball onto the foam block so that a clear, circular dent is made in the foam. Without

(continued)

Kinetic Energy *(continued)*

denting the foam further, mark your initials in the foam near the dent you just made. Also mark the height of the drop in meters ($\frac{1}{2}$ in this case).

3. Repeat step 2, dropping the golf ball from a height of 1 meter (approximately 40 inches). You may want to practice dropping the golf ball on a target from this height before putting unnecessary dents in the foam block. Again, mark the dent with your initials and the drop height.

4. Repeat step 2 with a drop height of 2 meters (approximately 79 inches). You may need to use a stepstool or ladder for this. If you use a ladder, be sure to follow any safety instructions printed on the ladder, and have another member of your group hold the ladder steady.

5. After each member of your group has carried out steps 1 through 4, each of you should measure the diameter of your foam dents to the nearest .1 cm(1 mm), and enter the results in your Data Collection and Analysis section. If a dent is elliptical rather than circular, measure both the longest and shortest "diameters" of the ellipse, and enter the average of the two as your result.

6. There is no simple formula to convert the diameter of a dent into a measure of the energy that made the dent. You can get an approximate result by raising each measured dent diameter to the fourth power. To do this using a calculator, enter the diameter, square it, and then square that result. Enter the final value in the Data Collection and Analysis section under "Energy." Don't worry about the units.

7. Make a graph of the "Energy" you calculated versus the height of the drop, with height on the horizontal axis and "Energy" on the vertical axis. Use a range of 0 to 2 meters for the horizontal axis and a range of 0 to 200 for "Energy."

EXTENSION

Calculate the work done on the golf ball as you raise it from the top surface of the foam to each of the three heights in the activity. Remember that Work = Force × Distance and that the force in this case is the weight of the golf ball. Use the balance to measure the mass of the golf ball in kg. Then multiply this by 9.8 m/s^2 to get the ball's weight in newtons.

DATA COLLECTION AND ANALYSIS

If your tape measure reads in inches, convert to meters (1 m = 39.4 inches).

Drop height __0.5__ m   dent diameter _____ cm   "Energy"_____

Drop height __1.0__ m   dent diameter _____ cm   "Energy"_____

Drop height __2.0__ m   dent diameter _____ cm   "Energy"_____

EXTENSION

Mass of golf ball _____ kg × 9.8 m/s^2 = Weight of golf ball _____ newtons

Work done to raise golf ball to 0.5 m _____ N-m

Work done to raise golf ball to 1 m _____ N-m

Work done to raise golf ball to 2 m _____ N-m

(continued)

Kinetic Energy *(continued)*

❓ CONCLUDING QUESTIONS

1. How does the value of the "Energy" you calculated vary according to the height from which the ball is dropped? _____

   _____

   _____

2. If you repeated this experiment with a golf ball having only half the mass of the original golf ball, would you expect that your values of "Energy" would be different? If so, how?

   _____

   _____

   _____

3. This activity assumes that all of the golf ball's kinetic energy goes into making the dent. How might you know if this is true or not? Did your experience in doing this activity indicate any leftover energy after the ball struck the foam? If so, what was the evidence? (You may repeat the experiment to refresh your memory if you wish.) _____

   _____

   _____

   _____

➡ EXTENSION

How should the following quantities compare with one another?

(a) the work done by you on the golf ball to raise it to a certain height

(b) the potential energy of the golf ball before you drop it from that height

(c) the kinetic energy of the golf ball dropped from that height, just before it hits

_____

_____

_____

〰 Follow-up Activity 〰

Find and list examples of objects with significant amounts of kinetic energy. Look for things with (a) a large mass and (b) a high velocity. A feather resting on a table would not be a good example.

Potential Energy

 INSTRUCTIONAL OBJECTIVES

Students will be able to

- describe the concept of potential energy.
- demonstrate creation of potential energy by doing work.

 NATIONAL SCIENCE STANDARDS ADDRESSED

Students demonstrate an understanding of

- properties of matter.
- motions and forces.
- relevant concepts to explain observed phenomena.

Students demonstrate scientific inquiry and problem-solving skills by

- framing questions.
- identifying and controlling variables in experimental settings.

Students demonstrate effective scientific communication by

- arguing from evidence and data.

 **MATERIALS**

- Bathroom scale
- A supply of books, either hardcover or softcover
- Table or bench
- Meterstick or tape measure

HELPFUL HINTS AND DISCUSSION

Time frame: 40–50 minutes
Structure: Individuals
Location: In class or at home

There is a close relationship between the concepts of *work* and *potential energy*. This activity should ordinarily be assigned after "Work (the Physics Kind)." Students who do the extension may be tempted to jump to an incorrect conclusion. Urge them to think carefully about this one.

ADAPTATIONS FOR HIGH AND LOW ACHIEVERS

High Achievers: Encourage these students to do the Extensions and the Follow-Up Activity.
Low Achievers: Review the relevant concepts, such as force and weight, for these students.

SCORING RUBRIC

Full credit can be given to students who correctly calculate the changes in potential energy and answer the questions correctly and in complete sentences. The quiz can be scored from 1 to 4 correct.

 INTERNET TIE-IN   http://www.glenbrook.k12.il.us/gbssci/phys/Class/energy/energytoc.html

QUIZ
1. Define potential energy.
2. What will happen to the gravitational potential energy of a rock if it is moved from one place to another on a flat, level table?
3. When an object falls from a higher altitude to a lower one, does it *gain* or *lose* gravitational potential energy?
4. List three forms of potential energy.

Potential Energy

 BEFORE YOU BEGIN

Objects can possess energy in many forms. Sometimes that energy is in storage, waiting to be released. Such energy is called **potential energy**. Stored potential energy can come in chemical, electrical, and other forms. A common form of potential energy is **gravitational** potential energy. Near the earth's surface, an object's gravitational potential energy increases with altitude. If you move a rock from the bottom of a hill to the top you *increase* its gravitational potential energy.

In most cases we need to consider only *changes* in gravitational potential energy. If you drop the rock, the increase in its kinetic energy (energy of motion) while it is falling is equal to the decrease in its potential energy. The change in gravitational potential energy of an object is equal to its weight multiplied by the change in its altitude. If the rock weighs 2 newtons and the hill is 100 meters high, the change in the rock's gravitational potential energy is:

Change in Potential Energy = Weight × (Change in Altitude)

For the rock, the change in potential energy is 2 newtons × 100 meters, or 200 newton-meters. Since the top of the hill is at a higher altitude than the bottom, the rock *gains* gravitational potential energy as it is moved up the hill.

Potential energy is a scalar quantity. Like work, the change in gravitational potential energy has the form **force × distance**. In fact, lifting an object does work on it and increases its gravitational potential energy. When an object is moved to a lower altitude, it releases this energy. The change in the object's potential energy is now negative.

 MATERIALS

- Bathroom scale
- A supply of books, either hardcover or softcover

- Table or bench
- Meterstick or tape measure

 PROCEDURE

1. Using the scale, weigh out about 20 pounds of books. Measure the actual weight, convert it to newtons, and enter the figure in the Data Collection and Analysis section. Set any extra books you have aside. Place the 20 pounds of books on the floor near the table in two or three piles.
2. Move the books onto the table, keeping them in the same piles. Measure and record the height of the table above the floor.
3. Compute the change in potential energy of the books, and enter your result in the space provided in the Data Collection and Analysis section.

▶ **EXTENSION**

Repeat step 2 in a building with several stories, starting with the books on the floor of the lowest story. Move the books up several stories, working quickly but safely. Make more than one trip to do this if you wish. When all the books are on the upper story, return them to their starting point on the lowest story. Measure, look up in building plans, or estimate the distance between lowest story and upper story. In the Data Collection and Analysis section, record the net change in altitude from the beginning to the end of this step and the weight of the books. Calculate and record the change in potential energy of the books.

(continued)

Potential Energy *(continued)*

DATA COLLECTION AND ANALYSIS

If your scale reads in pounds, convert to newtons (1 pound = 4.45 N).
If your tape measure reads in inches, convert to meters (1 m = 39.4 inches).

Weight of books   _____ N

Height of table   _____ m

Change in potential energy   _____ N-m

EXTENSION

Weight of books   _____ N

Net change in altitude of books   _____ m

Change in potential energy   _____ N-m

CONCLUDING QUESTIONS

1. What property of the books did you change? Did you increase or decrease it? _____

   _____

2. How much work did you do on the books to achieve this? _____

   _____

3. If you slide the books to another place on the same table, what happens to their potential energy?

   _____

EXTENSION

How did you feel immediately after performing the Extension on the previous page, compared with immediately after step 2? How much work (the physics kind) did you do by moving the books up several stories and down again? (**Hints:** Where did the books end up compared with where they started? You could also consider the upward and downward movements of the books separately, and think carefully about the work done, either positive or negative.) _____

_____

_____

🖐 Follow-up Activity 🖐

Find and list examples of objects with potential energy. As a guide, look for things that would change position or shape if some constraint were removed. For example, a rubber band stretched between your fingers has potential energy that can be released by letting go of the rubber band.

 Walch Hands-on Science Series: Force and Motion

INSTRUCTIONAL OBJECTIVES

Students will be able to

- describe the concepts of electric and magnetic forces.
- demonstrate the changes in electric and magnetic force with distance.

 NATIONAL SCIENCE STANDARDS ADDRESSED

Students demonstrate an understanding of

- properties of matter.
- motions and forces.
- momentum.
- relevant concepts to explain observed phenomena.

Students demonstrate scientific inquiry and problem-solving skills by

- framing questions.
- identifying and controlling variables in experimental settings.

Students demonstrate effective scientific communication by

- arguing from evidence and data.

 MATERIALS

Figure 1

PART A
- Balloon
- Tissue paper

PART B
- Spring scale (range 0 to 5 kilograms preferred)
- Strong magnet ("horse-shoe" magnet preferred)
- Steel block at least as big as the face of the magnet used
- Piece of solid (not stranded) copper wire about 20 cm long
- Table or bench
- Assorted "C" clamps
- Sheet of paper, $8\frac{1}{2}" \times 11"$
- One sheet of graph paper (extension activity)

spring scale

copper wire

magnet

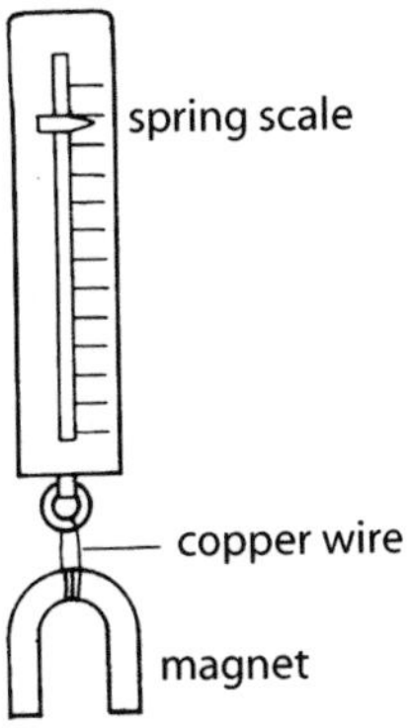

HELPFUL HINTS AND DISCUSSION

Time frame: 40–50 minutes, or one class period
Structure: Individuals
Location: In class or at home

For Part B, perform this activity beforehand to make sure the range of the spring scale matches the strength of the available magnet. Test the magnets and spring scales, and set them up in matched pairs. If the available magnets are not horseshoe shaped, you may need to determine which part of each magnet is strongest by testing with the steel block and figure out how to attach the copper wire so that the strong part of the magnet faces the steel block.

ADAPTATIONS FOR HIGH AND LOW ACHIEVERS

High Achievers: Encourage these students to do the Extensions and the Follow-Up Activity.

Low Achievers: Have reference books available that explain the relevant concepts. Review the use of a spring scale with these students.

SCORING RUBRIC

Full credit can be given to students who answer the questions correctly and in complete sentences. The quiz can be scored from 1 to 4 correct.

Figure 2

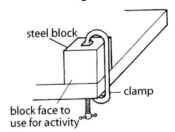

steel block

clamp

block face to use for activity

INTERNET TIE-INS   http://www.science.urich.edu/~rubin/pedagogy/131/131notes/131notes_69.html
http://www.altered-states.net/trifield/magdone.htm

 **QUIZ**   1. True or false: All atoms contain positive and negative electric charges.
2. How does the electric force between two charges depend on the distance between them?
3. What are the two poles of magnets called?
4. What will happen when you bring two of the same kind of magnetic poles together?

Electric and Magnetic Forces

 BEFORE YOU BEGIN

Electricity and magnetism are all around you. Much of our modern lifestyle is made possible by harnessing these forces. Motors, air conditioners, refrigerators, video games, CD players, computers, telephones, and televisions would not exist without the understanding and use of electricity and magnetism.

All matter is made of atoms. All atoms contain **positive** and **negative charges**. Electric forces come from the interaction between these charges. Two charges of the same kind—for example, a positive and a positive—**repel** each other. Two opposite charges, one positive and one negative, **attract** each other. The strength of the attraction or repulsion depends on the number of charges involved and on the distance between those charges. The greater the number of charges, the greater the force. The greater the distance between charges, the *lower* the force. This behavior is the key to all electrical interactions.

Magnetic forces come from interactions between *moving* charges. In a permanent magnet, like the ones on your refrigerator or the ones you will use in this activity, the charges are moving inside atoms on a microscopic scale. Magnets have two **poles**, called **north** and **south**. Two magnetic poles of the same kind repel, while opposites poles attract.

 MATERIALS

PART A
- Balloon
- Tissue paper

PART B
- Spring scale (range 0 to 5 kilograms preferred)
- Strong magnet ("horseshoe" magnet preferred)
- Steel block at least as big as the face of the magnet used
- Piece of solid (not stranded) copper wire about 20 cm long
- Table or bench
- Assorted "C" clamps
- Sheet of paper, $8\frac{1}{2}" \times 11"$
- One sheet of graph paper (extension activity)

 PROCEDURE

PART A

1. Inflate the balloon and tie it off. Tear off 10 to 20 small (less than 1 cm) pieces of tissue and place them on any flat surface.

2. Rub the balloon vigorously on your hair for 5 to 10 seconds. Then bring the balloon near to the tissue pieces without allowing them to touch. Observe what happens, and record your observations in the Data Collection and Analysis section.

Figure 1

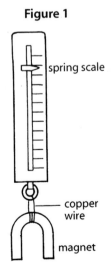

spring scale

copper wire

magnet

(continued)

Electric and Magnetic Forces *(continued)*

PART B

1. Using the copper wire, securely attach the moving part of the spring scale to the magnet so that the ends of the "U" shape point away from the scale. See Figure 1. Keep the magnet close to the spring scale, and use several turns of wire.

2. Securely mount the steel block to the bench using the clamp, as shown in Figure 2.

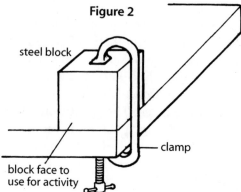

Figure 2

3. Stick the ends of the magnet onto the face of the steel block. Hold the spring scale horizontal. While observing the reading on the scale, slowly and gently pull the upper part of the spring scale horizontally away from the steel block until the magnet comes free of the steel. Practice until you get a reliable measurement of the force at which the magnet breaks free. Record this force in newtons in the space provided in the Data Collection and Analysis section.

steel block

clamp

block face to use for activity

4. Fold the sheet of paper in half to make two thicknesses of paper. Repeat step 3 with this paper *between* the magnet and the steel plate, and record your results.

5. Fold the paper in half again to make four thicknesses of paper. Repeat step 3 with this paper between the magnet and the steel plate, and record your results.

 EXTENSION

Using the graph paper, make a graph of the force versus the separation of the magnet and the steel block. Plot distance on the *x*-axis in units of paper thicknesses, from 0 to 4. On the vertical axis, plot the force reading from the spring scale. Connect your data points with straight lines.

DATA COLLECTION AND ANALYSIS

PART A

Observation of what happens when you bring the balloon near the tissue pieces (without allowing them to touch). _____

_____

PART B

If your scale reads in pounds, convert to newtons (1 pound = 4.45 N).
If your scale reads in kilograms, convert to newtons (1 kilogram = 9.8 N).

Thicknesses of paper	Force of magnet on steel block
0	_____ N
2	_____ N
4	_____ N

(continued)

Electric and Magnetic Forces *(continued)*

? CONCLUDING QUESTIONS

PART A

1. What happens to the tissue? Why didn't it happen when the balloon was far from the pieces of tissue? Once you've done step 2, what must be true about the charges on the balloon and the tissue? _____

   _____

2. From your experience with electric forces in this activity, what do you think the force would be, approximately, between any two charges that are extremely far apart?

   _____

   _____

PART B

1. Assuming that the sheet of paper has a constant thickness, the number of thicknesses of paper indicates the distance between the magnet and the steel. What happens to the force required to pull the magnet from the steel as the distance between the magnet and the steel is increased?

   _____

   _____

2. From your experience with magnetic forces in this activity, what do you think the force would be, approximately, between any two magnetic objects that are extremely far apart?

   _____

   _____

➪ EXTENSION

According to your graph, describe how the magnetic force in this particular case changes with distance. _____

   _____

   _____

⚞ Follow-up Activity ⚟

In the real universe, electric and magnetic forces fall off quickly as distance increases. This is fortunate. Imagine a world in which these forces did *not* decrease with distance. Describe some of the problems that might occur.

Share Your Bright Ideas with Us!

We want to hear from you! Your valuable comments and suggestions will help us meet your current and future classroom needs.

Your name_____Date_____

School name_____Phone_____

School address_____

Grade level taught_____Subject area(s) taught_____Average class size_____

Where did you purchase this publication?_____

Was your salesperson knowledgeable about this product?   Yes_____   No_____

What monies were used to purchase this product?

____School supplemental budget   ____Federal/state funding   ____Personal

Please "grade" this Walch publication according to the following criteria:

Quality of service you received when purchasing ....A   B   C   D   F
Ease of use...A   B   C   D   F
Quality of content..A   B   C   D   F
Page layout ....A   B   C   D   F
Organization of material ....A   B   C   D   F
Suitability for grade level...A   B   C   D   F
Instructional value...A   B   C   D   F

COMMENTS:_____

_____

What specific supplemental materials would help you meet your current—or future—instructional needs?

_____

Have you used other Walch publications? If so, which ones?_____

May we use your comments in upcoming communications?   ____Yes   ____No

Please **FAX** this completed form to **207-772-3105**, or mail it to:

Product Development, J.Weston Walch, Publisher, P.O. Box 658, Portland, ME 04104-0658

We will send you a **FREE GIFT** as our way of thanking you for your feedback. **THANK YOU!**